THE SEARCH
EXTRATERRESTRIAL
INTELLIGENCE

THE SEARCH FOR
EXTRATERRESTRIAL
INTELLIGENCE

Edward Ashpole

BLANDFORD

First published in the UK 1989 by
Blandford Press
An imprint of Cassell, Artillery House,, Artillery
Artillery Row, London SW1P 1RT

Reprinted 1990

Paperback edition 1990

Distributed in the United States by
Sterling Publishing Co, Inc.
2 Park Avenue, New York, NY 10016

Distributed in Australia by
Capricorn Link (Australia) Pty Ltd
PO Box 665, Lane Cove, NSW 2066

British Library Cataloguing in Publication Data
Ashpole, Edward
   The search for extraterrestrial intelligence
   1. Intelligent extraterrestrial intelligence
   I. Title
   574.999

ISBN 0 7137 1963 X (Hardback)
ISBN 0 7137 2210 X (Paperback)

Typeset by Inforum Ltd, Portsmouth

Printed in the UK by Biddles of Guildford

CONTENTS

To my old Mother and Aunt who thought that 'extraterrestrials is something to do with your stomach' – and to my wife, Patricia, without whose help this book would have been completed years ago!

Acknowledgements

'I hold every man a debtor to his profession,' wrote Francis Bacon (1561–1626). Anyone writing about science would certainly agree with that. I could write a bookful of acknowledgements, but of necessity I must be brief.

My thanks therefore to those who generously provided their time and assistance. They include Greg Barr, the National Space Society; Dr F. Biraud, the Observatoire de Paris; Professor Stuart Bowyer, University of California; Dr George Gatewood, University of Pittsburgh; Professor Hans Klapdor, the Max-Planck Institute for Nuclear Physics, Heidelberg; Gregg E. Maryniak, the Space Studies Institute, Princeton; Professor J. William Schopf, University of California; Charles L. Seeger, the SETI Institute, Los Altos, California; Zaqueline Souras, California Institute of Technology, Infrared Processing and Analysis Center; Dr Jill Tarter, University of California.

The staff of some organisations have provided help on numerous occasions. They include the British Museum (Natural History), London; the Centre National de la Recherche Scientifique; the Jet Propulsion Laboratory; the Martin Marietta Corporation; the Science and Engineering Research Council.

I am greatly indebted to all those people and organisations that have allowed me to reproduce their photographs and drawings. Here I should thank artist Francis Payne for her excellent work.

Thanks, also, to my Editor, Stuart Booth, whose wise and experienced council has always been available during the production of this book. And lastly, my special thanks to Dr Robert Dixon, who directs the world's longest running SETI observational program, for reading this book and providing the Foreword.

List of Illustration Acknowledgements

Colour and black and white illustrations

National Museum of Natural Sciences, Ottawa, plates 1 and 2; British Museum (Natural History) plate 3; Professor George Pilleri, University of Berne, plate 5; European Southern Observatory, plate 7; Science & Engineering Research Council, plates 6, 9 (Dr Hilary Evans), 13, 14 and 24; Professor J. William Schopf, plate 8; Dr John Cope, University College of Swansea, plate 10; Jet Propulsion Laboratory, plates 12 (Richard Terrile and Bradford Smith), 6, 13, 14, 15, 16, 17, 18, 22 and 23; NASA, plates 19, 22, 23 and 27; Professor Stuart Bowyer, University of California, plate 20; Dr F. Biraud, Observatoire de Paris, plate 21; SETI Institute, plate 25; Martin Marietta Corporation, plate 26; National Space Society, plate 26a.

Drawings

Icarus, pp. 30, 31; *Sky & Telescope*, p. 36; *ICI Magazine*, p. 40; adaptation from NASA material, p. 69; Centre National de la Recherche Scientifique, p. 81; Jet Propulsion Laboratory, p. 82; Cornell University (Frank Drake and Carl Sagan), p. 98; Hughs Research Laboratory, p. 111; Professor Gerard O'Neill, pp. 118, 121, 123, 127; Synergetic Press Inc., pp. 124, 125; NASA, p. 136; Sidgwick & Jackson Ltd: from 'The Sirius Mystery' by Robert K.G. Temple, p. 150.

Foreword

SETI is a science which has only just begun, in terms of what most involved scientists see as the tasks before them. Even though a number of searches have taken place for evidence of extraterrestrial intelligence, the searchers themselves would agree that the surface is yet to be scratched. The magnitude of the search needed is gigantic, and may require generations of scientific effort. Patience and persistence over the long-term are a prerequisite, since quick success is unlikely to be achieved.

Yet SETI is today poised at just the right moment to take a great leap forward. Man's electronic ingenuity is providing an accelerating spiral of more powerful yet less expensive capabilities in communications and computing technology — exactly the combination required for SETI. We are indeed fortunate that these tools are coming into existence just at the very time we need them. Even today these advances in computing capability are being exploited in programs such as those in progress at Harvard and those being planned by NASA. The next generation of searches will marry both modern computing *and* communications technologies to achieve even greater performance.

Every endeavour has its detractors. There are otherwise learned people who scoff in the background, yet have not bothered to read the scientific literature and ignore the relevant activities of prestigious world organisations such as the International Astronomical Union and the International Astronautical Federation. There are those who believe the fledgling past searches are definitive and hence we should give up now. There are also a few sincere researchers who believe that theory alone can solve the problem out of existence, making any actual searching or experimentation unnecessary. Fortunately, our scientific ranks contain many doers who are not content to sit back and do nothing, so they will always press on regardless.

The definition of 'success' for SETI as being the discovery of another civilisation is too superficial. There are deeper and less obvious levels of sucess. It is almost axiomatic that any kind of new wide-ranging scientific observations will discover hitherto unknown phenomena (eg. pulsars could have been discovered much earlier by both radio and optical astronomers, but nobody thought to look for pulsing signals). Since SETI strains the state of the electronic art, it leads to new technology which is applicable to other brands of astronomy, as well as to other fields. And at its deepest level, SETI provokes and influences the thoughts of Man. Even if no signals are ever found, SETI will always be a source of mental stimulation toward the perception by everyone of their personal and national position in the universe. Man must achieve this perception if he is to put aside his internal squabbles and create his own planet-wide civilisation. If this does not happen, and if this behaviour is universal, then SETI in the superficial sense can never succeed because there may never be two civilisations alive at the same time. If this *does* happen, then SETI in the deepest sense will be a success, and SETI in the superficial sense will be possible.

For the past fifteen years, a SETI program has been in progress here at The Ohio State University. During that time, many unexplained signals have been received. But 'unexplained' does not necessarily mean 'from another civilisation'. We do not know if they came from another civilisation, or from our own civilisation or from no civilisation. The problem is that the signals last only a short time — too short to tell where they are coming from, in detail. Later experiments to measure them more carefully never find anything. Similar signals have been found by other searchers.

These unexplained signals have led us to supplement the normal search techniques with additional ones that are used only when a signal is detected. This is an adaptive strategy, wherein all signals are investigated in detail immediately after their discovery, while they are still present. The normal search is temporarily suspended for as long as necessary. This new system will likely be in operation by the time you read this.

Of longer-range importance, we have begun to design the next generation of SETI programs. An all-electronic telescope (no big steel structures, etc.) will watch the entire sky all at once. This eliminates the need to 'point' a telescope at a specific spot in the sky, and thereby miss anything interesting that might be going on somewhere else. We have dubbed this the Argus telescope, after the mythological being that had a hundred eyes and could look in all directions at once. It is also interesting that Arthur C. Clark, in one of his works, gave the name Argus to a SETI telescope that could look in all directions at once. As of this writing, we have successfully operated a small pilot version of Argus, and are seeking support to build a large one.

I find this book to be a thoughtful exposition of current scientific thinking on SETI. Edward Ashpole maintains a reasonable perspective and a healthy skepticism of fringe subjects such as UFOs. He presents several new ideas of his own. The book should be of interest not only to the general reader, but to many scientists as well.

ROBERT S. DIXON
Columbus, Ohio. September 19, 1988

SETI . . . By Way of Introduction

OUR VIEW OF life and the universe goes far beyond that enjoyed by any previous generation, yet this fact is not always properly appreciated. An encounter I had with a Soviet space engineer some years ago provides an amusing illustration of this. He was sitting amidst a display of Soviet spacecraft at the Russian Exhibition in London, the first time that a full range of Soviet spacecraft had been shown in Britain. 'Has it been a successful exhibition?' I asked. He looked a little sad. 'The people here,' he said, 'are not much interested in the universe or space travel. Here I am to answer questions, but what do they all ask me? They ask "Please, can you tell me the way to the toilets?" '

Like the Russian Exhibition, this book is for a general audience. It also looks at the universe and space travel (and at life) in an attempt to answer the question: 'Can we find evidence of intelligence beyond the Earth?' But before we search for broadcasts from the stars, we have to look at a lot of information. And here is the immediate value of thinking about extraterrestrial intelligence and how it may be detected. The background information we must consider comes from those aspects of science that best make us aware of the human situation. We have to take a very close look at ourselves to guess if anything like us has evolved elsewhere. And to anticipate *their* possible behaviour, in exploring space and transmitting information across the Galaxy, we must look at our own behaviour and development.

Many articles and books have been written in recent years about 'visitors from other worlds', though most come straight from the myth factories of the mind. We have accounts of humanoid aliens landing all over the world in flying saucers. And from biblical times, the angels who used to arrive in 'chariots of fire' have now become visiting extraterrestrials in

1

nuclear-powered spaceships. Visitations, of course, have always been reported in terms of the culture and beliefs of the time.

But the authors of popular accounts of 'visitors from other worlds', although stimulating widespread curiosity, have neglected the science that would relate to their subject. And the point is that what is now known about life and the universe, often makes 'visiting alien' stories at best highly suspect, and at worst completely ridiculous. This is one of the reasons why a situation exists in which there is hardly any connection between those who believe in visitors in flying saucers and the scientists who support an energetic search by radio for evidence of our possible neighbours in the Galaxy.

In this field the shift to scientific respectability has been remarkable. In little more than a couple of decades, the search for extraterrestrial intelligence (SETI has become the accepted abbreviation) has moved from one which only science fiction writers explore to a central question for science itself. And nowadays SETI draws eminent scientists, in a range of disciplines, to large international conferences.

My own interest in life on other worlds goes back to the time when, as a young lad just before World War 2, I used to see Flash Gordon every Saturday morning at the local cinema. The simplicity of his space travel could not have been further from the future reality. His visits to the planets were made on the spur of the moment. An old scientist, wide-eyed and clearly raving mad, had built a spaceship in his back garden and needed a crew. (In those cinema days all scientists on the screen were old and mad.) So, off they went to save the world, or something equally grand, invariably accompanied by a glamorous female who was being repeatedly rescued by Flash Gordon from the unwelcome attentions of sinister Martians and alien monsters.

The planets they visited were populated by sharp-toothed prehistoric reptiles and beings indistinguishable from *Homo sapiens*. The *Homo sapiens*, divided neatly into 'goodies' and 'baddies', fought one another with a strange mixture of weapons technology (swords and rayguns) – Flash Gordon, unlike more conventional astronauts, was very good with a sword. And when the *Homo sapiens* were not fighting one another, they were fighting the reptiles. They were great movies, for a small boy, and I never missed a Saturday morning.

More in touch with scientific reality in those pre-war days was a science magazine called *Modern Wonder* to which the boy next door sold me a subscription. The magazine had a healthy sprinkling of astronomy and science fiction among more mundane features, which I never read, on subjects such as how a telephone or an electric train works. Somehow the insides of telephones and train engines never sparked my imagination like the Frogmen who lived on a tiny planet hidden permanently behind the Moon. You could hide anything behind the Moon at that time with no fear of being contradicted by NASA's next mission.

Among my fragmentary memories of *Modern Wonder* is an article, one of a series, on the shape of things to come. Its subject was 'When will men fly to the Moon?', and its prediction (in 1938) was for 1968! It was a little wide of the future reality because it assumed that Moon trips would quickly become something anyone could take, like a scheduled flight from London to New York; but it was not so wrong as the scientists at a symposium in Washington in 1937 who concluded that we would never fly to the Moon. Even when the space age had arrived, the eleventh Astronomer Royal, Sir Richard Woolley, was describing manned space travel as 'bilge' (which provoked a member of his staff to program the Observatory's computer to print out 'bilge' whenever its input was unsatisfactory). I remember one of the *Modern Wonder* illustrations which showed people queuing for the Moon Bus, and I did a little arithmetic on the kitchen table to see if I might still be around in 1968 – not, perhaps, to join the queue but to learn from others what it was like on the Moon.

The Moon has been tremendously important to our species. More than anything it has pulled us into space. The Moon was just far enough away and just near enough to be a challenge at the right time, when President Kennedy was looking for a venture to inspire the American people. It is a perfect stepping stone into the Solar System and a civilisation without a Moon might be far slower to launch itself into space.

But even in *Modern Wonder* days, the Moon was seen as a dead world. My interest in astronomy was largely stimulated by what 'old school' science fiction writers were interested in when they looked out into the universe: in life on other worlds. Astronomy offered the only way to knowledge of other worlds, and astronomers at that time offered in their popular books the only scientific speculations published on life beyond the Earth. Biologists in those days didn't ever think about such things. Life on Earth was enough for them. And for most people, despite the work of Copernicus four centuries earlier, the Earth still seemed to be the centre of the universe. No one guessed that within a few years science and technology would be examining the planets at close quarters and searching for extraterrestrial life. One well-known astronomer, writing about Venus as late as 1957, the year of Sputnik One, said: 'What the surface of the planet may be like beneath its impenetrable muffler of vapour is a mystery which may perhaps never be solved.' Eighteen years later, the Soviet craft Venus 9 and 10 were sitting on the planet's stony landscape taking photographs. Since then Soviet craft have taken more photographs and the Americans have mapped the surface of Venus by radar from an orbiting spacecraft.

Although the contribution of the astronomers was both basic and indispensable to any speculation about life on other planets, biologists can offer just as much insight into the subject. Yet until recently, few biologists speculated about extraterrestrial life. Consequently, we have suffered a certain lack of appreciation of the problems involved. When we consider, for instance, the immense time-scale of organic evolution on Earth and compare it with our very recent arrival as a technological species, the prospect of advanced extraterrestrial life and its technology becomes somewhat awesome, even forbidding. We begin to wonder about the human position on the cosmic scale, and we conclude that we may be a long way down that scale, somewhere near the bottom for a technological species. And looking out into the universe we begin to feel rather like Sir Fred Hoyle's 'perfectly good cod swimming off Yarmouth pier which haven't the faintest idea of what goes on in Yarmouth'.

Fortunately, this feeling has never inhibited science fiction writers. Has there ever been a human space traveller in fiction who worried about the cosmic status of his IQ? The prospect of being too primitive to qualify for contact with the inhabitants of Planet-X never entered the minds of the astronauts of fiction from Flash Gordon to *Star Trek's* Captain Kirk.

How long will it be before we need face such an embarrassing problem, before we discover signs of extraterrestrial intelligence and get some idea of where we stand as a species? Maybe the truth will remain beyond our reach for many generations, until new levels of science and technology can reveal it to us. Maybe the truth is almost within our grasp. Meanwhile, in this book, we can consider a range of answers. If we do this we may find the right answer about intelligence beyond the Earth although, of course, we won't know which one it is.

Now let's look in more detail at the central question of this book: 'Where is everybody?'

1

The Question

ONE DAY, SOME friends of the great physicist Enrico Fermi were trying to persuade him, so the story goes, that an abundance of life and technological civilisations must exist on an almost limitless number of other worlds. 'OK,' he said, 'but where is everybody?' That was in 1943 and though much has happened since to make a convincing theoretical case for an abundance of life throughout the universe, we are still asking Fermi's question. But we are now able to offer possible answers and technology is available (mainly in radio astronomy) to begin to check our answers. What was – and still is – entertaining speculation has become firmly based in science and technology.

Fermi's question is tantalising. A mass of indirect evidence from widely different sources supports the probability that extraterrestrial life and civilisations do exist, yet no one has so far discovered any direct evidence. Not that we should expect direct evidence so soon; the search will not be easy and has only just begun.

Radio astronomers in the United States, the Soviet Union, Canada, France and West Germany have set up about 50 programs in the past 25 years, and several of these searches are still in progress. Intelligent signals have not yet been detected, although there have been some exciting false alarms. No one can say when success might come. It could be any day, within the next decade, a century hence or far in the future when giant telescopes will be operated in space.

Of course, to search effectively we must try to guess the correct answer to our question. A simple story illustrates the kind of situation we are in. One night before World War 2, Winston Churchill was leaving the House of Commons after a long debate on an unresolved question. Clement Attlee, who told this story, watched the great statesman depart. 'You know', said one of Attlee's colleagues, 'Winston has ten answers to this question – and *one* of them is right!' The current SETI

(Search for Extraterrestrial Intelligence)* question is like that. There are ten answers ready and one may be right, although we don't know which one. Perhaps we've not yet thought of all the possible answers, but we can only do our best with what we can think of at present and perhaps form a hypothesis or two which can be tested – remembering always that a hypothesis is only science if it can be tested.

OTHER WORLDS

The idea of the plurality of inhabited worlds is as old as ancient Hindu theology, but it has not always been a popular idea. In 1600, the philosopher Giordano Bruno was burned at the stake in Rome for persistently proclaiming it. Rudolf Thiel, an eminent modern historian of astronomy, calls Bruno 'The ecstatic herald of science, the man who thought through the Copernican system to its logical conclusion and first revealed its true grandeur'. Bruno, perhaps more than anyone, developed the ideas that followed the work of Copernicus and which are so much part of our own universal view.

'Copernicus had banished the Earth from the centre of the universe', wrote Thiel, 'Bruno now did the same for the Sun, intuitively he realized that the Sun was only a star, one among millions of other stars.' The stars were no longer points of light on a fixed celestial sphere which enclosed the whole universe, but suns separated by great distances. The concept of infinity in space was born.

As in Bruno's day, people everywhere have usually seen themselves as the special creation of God or gods, and the existence of alien beings of equal rank could not be allowed. Today, without an opinion poll, it would be difficult to say whether this view of ourselves or the belief in a plurality of inhabited worlds holds ascendancy. However, although we can never prove that we are the special creation of God, we can test Bruno's belief in the plurality of inhabited worlds.

---

* When the possibility of using the apparatus of astronomy to detect evidence of extraterrestrial intelligence was first suggested, the term CETI (Communication with Extraterrestrial Intelligence) was coined. More recently, however, the 'Communication' bit began to look over-ambitious and 'Search' was substituted.

Although the test is uncertain of success, there is a compensation. The background to the test consists of fundamental science that intimately relates to life and the universe. Therefore, while we speculate about extraterrestrial life and alien intelligence we cannot help but look more closely at the human situation. Even if we fail to detect messages from the stars, the insight we can gain into life and the universe and ourselves should be worthwhile.

TECHNOLOGY, EVOLUTION AND HABITATION

When we try to estimate the average longevity of extraterrestrial civilisations (a major factor in estimating their abundance and therefore our chances of detecting their presence) we have to look at our own chances of survival. We find ourselves asking questions such as 'Is technology taking us to extinction or to a golden age?' and 'How might we develop technology to increase our chances of survival?' It is ironic that as we search for life beyond the Earth, the survival of our species has never been more in doubt, as high technology and the natural instincts of man look increasingly uneasy together. We are becoming alarmingly like the Irish Elk, which became extinct because its antlers became too heavy for its head.

But what is the probability that technological civilisations with a desire to communicate (like ourselves) have ever existed? To try to answer that question, we must consider how large a part chance has played in our being here.

According to present-day biology, human beings (and all other species of animals and plants) are the children of chance. We must be unique in the universe, say the evolutionary biologists, because of the incalculable number of chance events that have made us what we are. Yet life and intelligence could be abundant in widely different forms. Like the formation of galaxies, of stars within galaxies, of the elements themselves, the build-up in molecular complexity that led to life on Earth appears to be inherent in the nature of the universe and in the nature of matter. Given enough time – and the universe offers plenty of time – we might expect other technological creatures to evolve on other planets, but none in our exact image.

Thanks to Charles Darwin and four generations of evolutionary biologists, we see ourselves as a unique animal species

9

among millions of other equally unique animal and plant species that have evolved on one favoured planet during the past four billion* years. But whether four billion years is a long or a short time for organic evolution to produce just one technological species we do not know, although theoretical research on the evolution of the Earth's atmosphere is beginning to show why it has taken so long.

Habitable Zones

Mathematical studies of the evolution of planetary atmospheres and the so-called habitable zones around stars indicate that advanced life may be restricted to planets and stars similar to the Earth and the Sun. The physical and chemical conditions essential for the origin of life and its evolution into advanced forms seem to depend upon a planet having about the same mass as the Earth. (We will consider this in more detail later.) And the star of a continuously habitable planet may have to be similar to the Sun: within a range of 80–120 per cent of the Sun's mass.

A planet for advanced life must also orbit its sun within a relatively narrow 'continuously habitable zone'. The Earth's orbit only just comes within such a zone, according to recent theoretical studies. Had the Earth been a few per cent closer to the Sun, it would have become early in its history a furnace like Venus. Had it been a little further away, it would have become a permanently frozen world like Mars. Therefore, Earth-type planets may not be as abundant as was thought several years ago, though the question we must ask is: 'Are they abundant enough to justify searches for signals from other civilisations?'

Here we meet an intriguing development of recent years. While astronomical research is showing that Earth-type planets may be much rarer than we thought, other developments are showing that their abundance or otherwise may not be relevant to the abundance of civilisations in the Galaxy.

The pioneering work of Gerard K. O'Neill, a professor of physics at Princeton University, and of his colleagues, has changed drastically our thinking about the need for habitable

---

* Throughout this book 'billion' means a thousand million (1,000,000,000). This is the American and French meaning of the word, and the one adopted by science. As the reader will see, it is a very useful term used in this sense.

Major Events in Life's History.

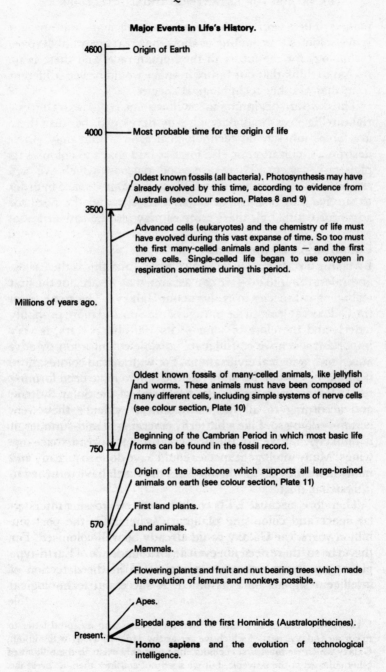

4600 — Origin of Earth

4000 — Most probable time for the origin of life

Oldest known fossils (all bacteria). Photosynthesis may have already evolved by this time, according to evidence from Australia (see colour section, Plates 8 and 9)

3500

Advanced cells (eukaryotes) and the chemistry of life must have evolved during this vast expanse of time. So too must the first many-celled animals and plants — and the first nerve cells. Single-celled life began to use oxygen in respiration sometime during this period.

Millions of years ago.

Oldest known fossils of many-celled animals, like jellyfish and worms. These animals must have been composed of many different cells, including simple systems of nerve cells (see colour section, Plate 10)

Beginning of the Cambrian Period in which most basic life forms can be found in the fossil record.

750

Origin of the backbone which supports all large-brained animals on earth (see colour section, Plate 11)

First land plants.

570

Land animals.

Mammals.

Flowering plants and fruit and nut bearing trees which made the evolution of lemurs and monkeys possible.

Apes.

Bipedal apes and the first Hominids (Australopithecines).

Present.

Homo sapiens and the evolution of technological intelligence.

planets. Their work on the development of space stations and space colonies is beginning to show the great potential of space technology for the future of the human race, and there is no reason to think that our future in space would be very different from that of other technological species.

Thus, we are beginning to see how some ETIs (extraterrestrial intelligences) may have already developed, because there are forces inherent in technological growth that may either destroy a civilisation or else force it into space to colonise its planetary system. There are good reasons, which we will examine later, to expect that ETIs will colonise space in order to survive and not just to satisfy curiosity and the need for adventure, although these motives may also be satisfied.

Colonisation of the Galaxy

By taking a statistical view of ourselves – and this is the easiest and safest thing to do – we can assume that we are not the first technological species to evolve in our Galaxy.* The great age of the Galaxy (at least twice the age of the Sun and more probably older), and therefore of some of its 100 billion stars, is very important when we consider its possible colonisation by advanced technological civilisations. For widespread colonisation, it would be enough for stars like the Sun to have been forming just a billion years before the formation of the Solar System, and according to all the astronomical evidence they were certainly doing so. Like a butterfly emerging in mid-summer, it is unlikely that we are the first creatures to spread space-age wings. Many intelligent species could have done so already and many more may do so when we and the Earth have returned to interstellar dust.

Therefore, because ETIs could have been crossing interstellar space and colonising planetary systems for the past few billion years, the Galaxy could already be well colonised. For this to be so, there need not even be an abundance of Earth-type planets, as some astronomers interested in the detection of intelligent signals once assumed. A successful technological

---

* Throughout this book I have written the Galaxy with a capital letter to mean *our* Galaxy, part of which we see as the Milky Way. It is life in our Galaxy which we must first consider. Life probably exists in the billions of other galaxies in the universe, but we need not consider them at present.

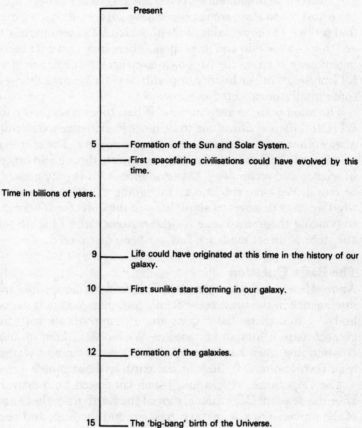

Time Enough to Visit the Solar System.

Present

Time in billions of years.

5 — Formation of the Sun and Solar System.

— First spacefaring civilisations could have evolved by this time.

9 — Life could have originated at this time in the history of our galaxy.

10 — First sunlike stars forming in our galaxy.

12 — Formation of the galaxies.

15 — The 'big-bang' birth of the Universe.

species might build its own habitats in space. So just one intelligent species might establish a vast number of civilisations, providing its space technology led to widespread interstellar travel. Personally, I can't envisage super intelligent beings using up their lives travelling across the Galaxy. But colonisation could conceivably be carried out by robots with high artificial intelligence and 'blueprints' of the super-being genetic code, so that copies of the 'home' species could be re-created anywhere in the Galaxy.

How probable all this may be we shall consider later. We shall also look at whether or not a state of colonisation in the

13

Galaxy is inconsistent with our present lack of evidence of extraterrestrial intelligence. As the Solar System has been open to visitors for so long, some people have suggested that we may find probes, or the remains of them, which ETIs sent here long ago to study the Sun and its planets. There may be a data bank, ingeniously sited on the Moon or elsewhere, or evidence of an ETI presence in our history or prehistory. Or we may discover some totally unexpected evidence.

The main point to keep in mind is that there is no reason for ETIs and their civilisations to be more in evidence today than at any other time in human history or prehistory. The search is on now only because we have become aware, through advances in science and technology, that evidence of ETIs may possibly be found. We have run into an intriguing situation because of what we have discovered about life and the universe. There is a convincing theoretical case for the existence of ETIs, but not one item of direct evidence has yet been discovered.

The Basic Question
Although we can now ask specific questions about life and intelligence in the universe, Fermi's question 'Where is everybody?' remains the basic question. It confronts us with the greatest gap in human knowledge. We have the kind of anticipation that must have preceded the Copernican and Darwinian revolutions: a feeling for the truth without proof.

The Copernican revolution, which continued for a century after the death of Copernicus, moved the Earth from the centre of the universe to a planetary orbit around the Sun, and thus changed our relationship to the universe. The Darwinian revolution, while shattering the intellectual peace of nineteenth-century Christian thought, changed our relationship to the rest of life on Earth, and to God, We who had remained aloof and distinctly separate as God's special creation became a part of nature and went on to discover our origins in nature.

The discovery of a technological intelligence elsewhere in the universe would lead us into a revolution in thought and attitudes no less drastic than those precipitated by Copernicus and Darwin. Indeed, the impact could be greater. Although we have been fed for years with science fiction and are used to having science fiction turned into science fact, the reality of actually knowing that *they* are out there would shock in a way that Copernicus and Darwin never did. Our relationship to life and the universe would be changed yet again. Also, and more than anything else, our relationship to humankind itself would be changed. The knowledge that non-human minds, which could be superior in ways we cannot imagine, were out there beyond the Solar System could make us more conscious of our own nature and predicament.

2

Ceilings

MOST OF US tend to look upon science as an unending source of knowledge, as something which will be applied in the continuous advance of technology for as long as human civilisations may last. Science fiction writers especially have helped to foster this view. Of course, we may destroy ourselves before we get very far, but otherwise the common view of the future is one overflowing with technological marvels.

We have been conditioned to think thus. So far, in our technological infancy, new science and technologies have crashed through the hypothetical barriers proclaimed previously by the cautious and the pessimistic. The curiosity of scientists and the inventiveness of technologists have been overwhelmingly triumphant. So much so that we begin to believe that this process will go on for ever, that there are no barriers to stop our technological advance; eventually almost everything will be possible.

A few years ago Carl Sagan suggested that it might not be possible to communicate with civilisations just a thousand years ahead of us. The differences between what we (or another species at our level) are today and what we may become in a thousand years of advancing science and technology could be unbridgeable. And the technologies of very advanced societies, said Sagan, may appear to us as magic.

Now it could be that Sagan is right. There may be no ceiling to applicable knowledge in our universe. An unending advance of technology may be possible. But to the human mind, at least, there must be a limit to everything. Today, most astronomers and physicists think that observations of the far regions of the universe indicate that it is finite. And the information contained in a finite universe must also be finite. So too would the information that would specify the nature of matter and the laws and forces which determine its behaviour. In turn, this would mean that there must be a ceiling to knowledge and to its

16

applications – a ceiling beyond which no species can go, regardless of how clever it may be. Thus, an important question for SETI projects is how high is this ceiling: low or unimaginably high?

Let us accept for a moment that an unimaginably high ceiling to knowledge actually exists. This would then permit the great future advances of science and technology that in science fiction have so coloured our picture of extraterrestrial civilisations. Then, indeed, many extraterrestrial technologies would appear to us as magic – if we ever saw them, which seems unlikely. But on the time-scale of organic evolution, 1,000 years is a mere instant. So, if we could not communicate with ETIs 1,000 years or more in our future, then the number of civilisations with which we could communicate virtually disappears. All colonial ETIs (if such there be), those established in alien planetary systems, would of necessity be at least thousands of years ahead of us. And it may be that it is the existence of many colonial civilisations that offers us our best chance of detecting evidence of ETIs. But only perhaps if the assumption of an unlimited future advance of science and technology is incorrect. The lower the ceiling of knowledge, the better must be the chance of detecting evidence.

Given our present rate of application to the task, it may be that the kind of fundamental knowledge of nature from which major new technologies can spring will be discovered in the next few centuries. In short, the scientific ceiling may be much lower than we have anticipated. Further discoveries may be made, but not discoveries of a fundamental, applicable kind. The basic structure and machinery of the universe, which we exploit so eagerly today, would be known. On that basis, the technologies of civilisations more than 1,000 years ahead of us, rather than appearing to us as magic, might be almost recognisable. In these circumstances, all technological ETIs, except the very latest arrivals, would be applying the same science, the same knowledge, to reach the same 'levels of technical perfectibility' in their various technologies. And they would reach the universal scientific and technological ceilings very early in their histories. In any case, given enough time, this situation seems inevitable for intelligent life – and inevitable whether the ceilings are very low or so high that present human intelligence could never reach them.

LIMITS TO THE HUMAN BRAIN

J.B.S. Haldane once said that 'The universe may not only be queerer than we imagine, but queerer than we *can* imagine.' We have only to consider how discoveries in astronomy have changed our view of the universe in the past 100 years to see that this is true in one sense. The universe that we know today is certainly 'queerer' than anyone could have imagined 100 years ago. But this is not what Haldane meant. He meant that the human brain may lack the capacity to comprehend the nature of the universe. In other words, the ceiling to complete understanding may be too high for us. There is, of course, no reason why we should expect to be able to comprehend the universe. We do not think it strange that the brain of a chimpanzee, our closest relative on Earth, cannot comprehend the universe. So why should we expect our brains to possess such an awesome capability? After all, we cannot claim that the human brain is more than a couple of orders of magnitude greater than the brains of the most advanced of the apes. Our brains are about three to four times larger than theirs, but a full understanding of the universe may need far more intelligence than any human can possess. Yet it does not follow that the universe will always be queerer than any level of intelligence can imagine, to use Haldane's words. Intelligence beyond our own may be capable of discovering all scientific knowledge, even if the ceiling is too high for us.

A great mystic and science fiction writer, Olaf Stapledon, wrote in *The Star Maker* in 1937: 'And this is the goal of all being, that the universe be known and admired and that it be bestowed with further beauties . . .' I copied Stapledon's words into a notebook some 30 years ago when I read *The Star Maker* and I have since lost the notebook. So I'm relying on memory here and I may have slightly misquoted him, yet what he wrote encapsulated my feelings at the time and it still does.

THE HUMAN FUTURE

How far does intelligence have to advance before the universe can be known? Whether human intelligence can do so or not we cannot say. Even its most gifted future members may not have sufficient intellectual capacity if the ceiling to knowledge is high. Alternatively, a very low ceiling would determine a future distinctly different from that allowed by a very high ceiling.

POSSIBLE FUTURES

Now the purpose of this speculation – our trying to guess the future of mankind – is to try to find clues to what kinds of signs to look for in the search for extraterrestrial civilisations. It can also guide us in assessing the probability of there being any signs at all for which to search.

Fundamentally, the future of mankind can go in only one of five ways:

1 early extinction;

2 the breakdown of civilisation and a return to permanent barbarism;

3 a cyclical future: barbarism – civilisation – barbarism – civilisation;

4 scientific and technological advance to a low universal ceiling, or to a level beyond which the brains of *Homo sapiens* or his descendants cannot go, followed by a long period of consolidation and stability;

5 continual scientific and technological advance to levels of civilisation unimaginable to us and probably beyond the capacity of the present human brain to understand, as Haldane predicted. This future could involve a far more intelligent human species, perhaps a different being altogether, and highly advanced artificial intelligence.

Obviously, the first three alternatives could be the future of any technological species, since technology brings biological success and over-population and opportunities to make increasingly effective weapons. Therefore, the choice of one of the last two alternatives is all that need concern us here. For all successful technological species – and it would apply to all – future 4 above could explain why no one has completely colonised the Galaxy – as far as we know. No species has been able to muster the energy and technology needed and no one ever will. Though considering our rapid advances in science

19

and space technology, at least some colonisation by other species seems inevitable. The occurrence of alternatives 1, 2 and 3 would obviously not contribute to colonisation, although they could hardly be the fate of everyone. But given future 5 for just one technological species during the past few million years (plus the will to use unlimited science and technology to explore and expand its civilisation) and the Galaxy should have been colonised.

Alternatively, although a very low scientific and technological ceiling (future 4) may take some of the thrill out of science and technology, and most of the thrill out of science fiction, it would have its compensations. No extraterrestrial civilisation would be so far ahead of us that we might not eventually catch it up. Interstellar communication by electromagnetic radiation (radio, light or another section of the electromagnetic spectrum) would be more likely to exist because the nature of the universe would probably not offer the basis for a better way. By this I mean that our physics would not have to advance for a few more centuries before we discover what we need to know in order to detect the messages of our intelligent neighbours in the Galaxy. And the most important of all considerations, our self-esteem would not be permanently crushed by knowing that we are no more than tenth-rate citizens of the Galaxy, or worse.

With very low ceilings the cultural gap between ourselves and any ETIs might be closed by *Homo sapiens*. Yet if ETIs are orders of magnitude beyond us in intelligence and ceilings hardly exist, then it would be like trying to close the gap between ourselves and Sir Fred Hoyle's 'perfectly good cod off Yarmouth Pier that have no idea about what goes on in Yarmouth'.

For us, I think, the existence of very low scientific and technological ceilings would be best. It would be a more comfortable universe for us, psychologically. The 'zoo hypothesis' that the Earth is kept as a sort of planetary nature reserve, protected from the impact of advanced civilisations, is not one we would wish to be correct. We don't want to be inmates of a zoo, no matter how well protected – though, of course, we don't mind putting our nearest primate relatives in zoos!

Most radiation from the universe never reaches the Earth's surface and the telescopes of ground-based astronomers.

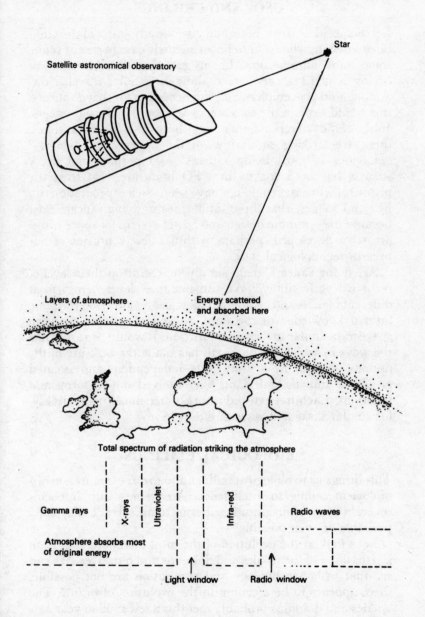

Star

Satellite astronomical observatory

Layers of atmosphere

Energy scattered
and absorbed here

Total spectrum of radiation striking the atmosphere

| Gamma rays | X-rays | Ultraviolet | Infra-red | Radio waves |

Atmosphere absorbs most
of original energy

Light window   Radio window

UFOs AND CEILINGS

Let us speculate freely here, and give the advocates of the UFO phenomenon, who seem to be losing their case in recent years, some more ammunition. Let us say that the technological ceiling is just high enough to allow interstellar travel. Now, although no proven physical evidence exists for flying saucers, this would explain the consistency in reports of flying saucers. In thousands of reports, including those from historical times, there are striking similarities in the appearance, size and behaviour of most flying saucers. And perhaps not every witness has been soaked in UFO literature – at least the historical witnesses could not have been. So let speculation run free and suggest that these similarities in flying saucers exist because the optimum design and power system for space travel are soon developed, perhaps within a few centuries of our present technological state.

Are flying saucers, then, simply spacecraft at their level of technical perfectibility? We can imagine clever beings from different planets and of different biologies all applying the same limited knowledge of the universe and all ending up with spacecraft similar in form and function. It would be rather like the ways in which life on Earth has made the best use of the options open to it, so that quite independent and isolated groups of animals and plants have evolved similar forms and functions. Each has evolved a sort of 'technical perfectibility' for similar tasks and ways of life.

BIOLOGICAL CEILINGS

This brings us to biological ceilings and to our examination of a biological ceiling to intelligence. Are beings with intellects several orders of magnitude superior to ourselves biologically probable or even possible?

Let's look at the evolution of the most advanced brains on Earth, those of the whales and dolphins and ourselves. We can see that where technology and civilisation are not possible, there appears to be a ceiling to the evolution of brains. The whales and dolphins probably met this a few million year ago. For example, the ancestors of the bottle-nose dolphin had already evolved their present brain size (as advanced in structure as ours and larger) a few million years ago, when our pre-human ancestors had brains no larger than those of present-day apes (see colour section).

Living as they do in a natural environment, the whales and dolphins would have evolved even bigger brains and more intelligence had it been advantageous so to do. But they had all the brain power they needed for their way of life. Of course, much of their spectacular brain development is probably used to 'see' by sound in their underwater world; this they may do as well as we see our world by light.

Human brains seem to have reached a peak about 50,000 years ago. But it is not just a matter of brain size. During our evolution from ape to man we must also have profited from the brain's improved internal organisation. For example, it looks as if the two hemispheres of the primate brain became less like duplicates and were used increasingly for separate functions, thus speeding up the evolution of our ancestors.

A natural environment with hazards to human life that demanded much greater mental powers than we possess is hard to envisage. And it does not seem likely that intellects much greater than ours could evolve by natural selection. Unless more intelligence had survival value, it would not evolve.

Could a slightly higher human intelligence have evolved had we not settled to agriculture and animal husbandry some 10,000 years ago? The answer from the human craniums of 50,000 years ago, which had on average a slightly larger capacity than today's craniums, is 'probably not'. In any case, as intelligence becomes greater, the onset of civilisation becomes more likely – and with it, as society develops, an end to further biological improvements by natural means.

Therefore we cannot assume that those super brains possessed by some extraterrestrials in science fiction are natural products. If they exist in reality, they will have been bred artificially, or produced by biological engineering, or be electronic rather than biological brains. But whatever their nature and origin, the super brains would have needed a level of beings like ourselves to take the first step towards producing them.

NEW HUMAN SPECIES

Would the human race, or biological ETIs, take such steps? Future generations may be forced to these actions as the management of their world becomes more complex; but the move towards higher intellect could be made slowly. Doubling the intellectual capacity of mankind every 1,000 years might not cause social, psychological or personal problems, although at the end of the period a new species of *Homo* would be controlling the planet Earth. In this way, our overwhelming instinct for self-preservation would not stop our eventual replacement by a higher grade of human beings.

Nevertheless, there must be a limit to how far a species may go biologically in improving its brain by artificial means. We would be limited to improving what already exists in the human brain. We could not expect to evolve artificially a neural structure and capacity that does not already exist in the human brain, in however an embryonic form. New neural structures, with new functions unknown and unimaginable beforehand, could only come into being by natural selection. And natural selection is a process in which most new developments perish when put on trial in the environment. We can hardly conceive that such ruthlessness would be adopted in selective breeding or in biological engineering. New individuals so produced would have to be sound and healthy and an improvement, however slight, on the previous generation. The trial-and-error method of nature, where the errors are ruthlessly eliminated, could hardly be undertaken by a humane society. We would therefore be limited to improving what nature already provides.

Another possible obstacle to 'super brains' concerns our DNA (deoxyribonucleic acid). The amount of our DNA, which specifies everything we are, including the structures and functions of the brain, might not be adequate for 'super brain' plans – whatever they might be. A human intellect way beyond what we possess, with new capabilities, would have to be specified by our DNA, and it may not be biologically possible. The super brains, if they exist outside science fiction, may therefore have a basis other than protoplasm. They may be electronic intelligences – taken, no doubt, to their limit of technical perfectibility.

FUTURE ELECTRONIC BEINGS

While we are speculating on a ceiling to brains and intelligence, we can hardly pass by a question often asked in science fiction: Would biological intelligence ever give way to electronic intelligence? Would we let the robots take over?

We might, as already suggested, give way to a higher form of man without defying our sense of self-preservation, providing it took place over a long enough period, say several dozen generations. Parents don't mind having children more intelligent than themselves. But we would never willingly retire in favour of a machine. Although we cannot speak for a higher form of humanity, we can guess that it would no more give way to artificial intelligence than we would. For as we are (genetically) still mainly ape, so they would possess our genetic endowment with just a little extra that would make them superior. Likewise, all biological ETIs, if they evolved by natural selection, would have self-preservation inexorably built into their genes. The super electronic brains would be created to serve, and would take over only by accident.

The biological ceiling for brains may therefore be low. And only the eletronic brains that escape from the control of biological brains, either through carelessness or intention, may have the powers described in science fiction – and no doubt a lot more besides. So, if anyone watches over the Galaxy, protecting us in a planetary zoo, it may be such artificial intelligences which, by this time in the history of the universe, may be forever beyond the understanding of biological beings.

Human brains, or the brains of other beings elsewhere, may become more advanced, by directed evolution or other means, and the capacity and quality of intellectual life be increased beyond anything we can imagine. Yet the technological capabilities of even the most advanced civilisations in the Galaxy must still be limited – ultimately – by the amount of applicable information in the universe. No matter how high the technological and biological ceilings are, somewhere they must exist.

Let us now look in some detail at the probability that enough planets like the Earth have existed to have made advanced ETIs and their civilisations possible.

3

Planets for Intelligent Life

THANKS TO GERARD O'NEILL's work on the future technologies of space colonies, we can see that ETI civilisations may not necessarily be restricted to planetary systems with habitable planets, 'blue planets' like the Earth, where life evolves for billions of years. Such planets may be much rarer than we thought only a few years ago. It is beginning to look as if planets that are continuously habitable (*continuously* is the key word) can evolve only where an exceptional set of conditions exist. Many planetary systems, differing little from the Solar System, may nowhere provide all these conditions and therefore offer no cradle for the origin and evolution of life.

Yet ETIs could nevertheless live in such planetary systems, secure in their own custom-built habitats which orbit stars that, for one reason or another, never sparked organic chemistry into life on any of their planets. Now it seems that most stars are either too massive or not massive enough for the evolution of planets which remain habitable for several billion years. And planets like Earth may be the rare places where technological civilisations are born and not permanent homes for their long-term growth and development. Moreover, lifeless worlds like the Moon, rather than being the sites of future civilisations, are more likely to be used as rich sources of building materials.

But what of the evolution of Earth-like planets? A successful technological species may colonise its own planetary system – this looks as certain a development as any that one can foresee – but the probability of it migrating to other planetary systems is a very different matter, involving as it would interstellar travel. And for all we know a whole planetary system may provide enough scope for the most energetic explorers, especially if the problems of interstellar travel are as great as we imagine. In any case, it does seem unlikely that highly intelligent beings with a wealth of interesting things to do at home, would

26

personally spend their lives crossing interstellar space when advanced automated spacecraft could do this for them.

We know that our planet has evolved from an ordinary star and that there are several billion stars like it in our Galaxy, and some billions of times that number in the observable universe. It looks as though the formation of planets may be a universal phenomenon, part of the development of at least a proportion of stars. But planets are very insignificant compared with the quantity of matter and energy involved in star formation: the planets are really mere debris. Yet even within the Solar System we see the planetary system phenomenon repeated. Look at Jupiter – sometimes called a 'failed star' – and its fascinating worlds in orbit; look also at the more distant gas giants – Saturn, Uranus and Neptune – and at their satellites.

The gas giants are probably little changed since their formation. Because of its great mass, and similar composition to the Sun, some astronomers have called Jupiter more a star than a planet – although Jupiter would have to be more than 50 times as massive to become the dimmest of red dwarf stars. This is the minimum mass necessary to make a star; there is not otherwise enough gravitational pressure and temperature for the nuclear fusion of hydrogen.

Whilst most astronomers believe that a vast number of stars throughout the universe do have planetary systems, the origin of the Solar System itself is still uncertain. For example, there is evidence that a supernova explosion increased the abundance of some elements in the gas cloud from which the Sun and planets formed. (A supernova is a star that explodes catastrophically due to instabilities following the exhaustion of its nuclear fuel, becoming for a few days up to 100 million times brighter than the sun.) Indeed, many astronomers think a supernova may have initiated the collapse of the cloud, as well as enriching it with heavy elements that can be synthesised only in such explosions. There is evidence for this in some meteorites that contain material which is older by about a billion years than the Solar System.

FORMATION OF PLANETS

Let us now take a brief look at the generally accepted theory of planetary formation. As the disc of gas around the primordial

Sun cooled, the substances in it changed from gas to liquids to solids. These first steps in planetary formation have been worked out extensively in theory – and in recent years the sequences of the condensations have been studied with the help of meteorites.

First, metals with a high boiling point and their compounds coagulated into small spheres. Next, the silicates (elements combined with oxygen and silicon) condensed out – and so on. Not until temperatures within the gas fell to a few hundred degrees did the more volatile substances begin to condense. Clumps of matter then built up by collisions. Some clumps became very large and gathered more matter by gravitational attraction. The process was a runaway one. And all the planets (except the gas giants and the eroded face of Earth) and many of their moons show evidence of the last great bombardment by large meteorites which ended about four billion years ago. Not that the bombardment has completely ended, of course.

Planets that formed near the Sun, therefore, consist predominantly of the less volatile substances (metals and silicates), whilst those further out (the gas giants) were formed mainly of the lighter elements. Also, the inner planets did not retain hydrogen and helium as they formed, although the primordial disc of gas around the Sun was mainly composed of these two lightest of the elements. Intense radiation from the Sun must have driven these gases from the inner planets. These light elements have been retained by the gas giants because of their high gravities and low temperatures. So it looks as if rocky planets (like Mercury, Venus, Earth and Mars) and gas giants (like Jupiter, Saturn, Uranus and Neptune) may be inevitable products of the way in which stars and their planets form.

There may be indirect evidence that other stars have planets. Some stars could be wobbling as they move across the sky, instead of moving in straight lines, due to the gravitational pull of large planets. Such planets cannot be detected directly by present techniques, but with observational astronomy going into space and benefitting from revolutionary new designs and electronic aids, astronomers may soon be able to observe the planets of the nearest stars.

Newspapers occasionally proclaim the discovery of a new solar system. People expect astronomers to be able to detect the

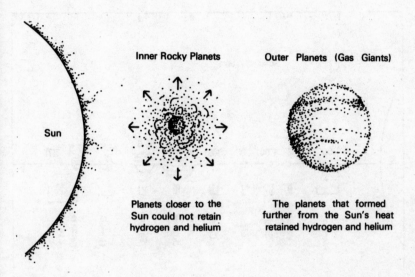

Inner Rocky Planets

Outer Planets (Gas Giants)

Sun

Planets closer to the
Sun could not retain
hydrogen and helium

The planets that formed
further from the Sun's heat
retained hydrogen and helium

We can now appreciate how the difference came about between the
inner 'rocky' planets and the outer 'gas giants', which are mostly
atmosphere with a rocky core. The hotter a gas becomes, the faster its
atoms move and the more difficult it is for them to be held by a
planet's gravity. Thus, as the inner planets formed, the Sun's heat
drove off most of the hydrogen and helium, the lightest and most
abundant of the elements. This did not happen as the gas giants
formed because of their great distances from the Sun. Also, as they
gathered up more and more matter their gravity became strong
enough to hold these elements permanently. Astronomers Donald
Goldsmith and Tobias Owen (see Recommended Books and Associations) have pointed out that 'The mass of the Earth would approximately equal the mass of Saturn if we added the missing hydrogen
and helium to our planet's present store of elements, in the same
proportion that we find in the Sun and the giant planets.'

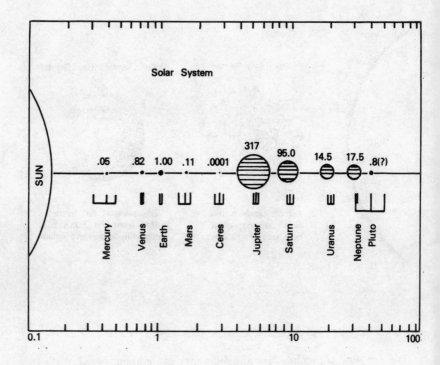

On the right we see a result from a computer experiment by Steven Dole on the origins of planetary systems. It shows a small sample of five planetary systems evolved by the computer program. The gas giants of each system (Jupiter is our largest gas giant) are shown by cross-hatching. The other planets are rocky planets like Mercury, Venus, Earth and Mars.

Distances from their parent stars are given in astronomical units (an astronomical unit is the average distance from Earth to the Sun). The trident markings show the variation in a planet's orbit, its closest, average and greatest distance from its parent star. The masses of planets are given as units of the Earth's mass.

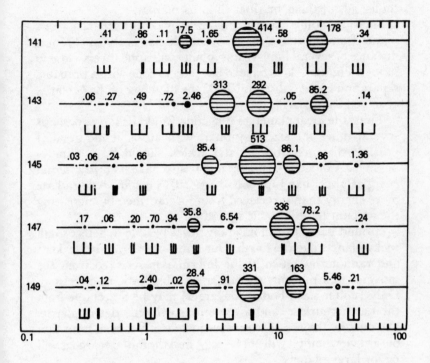

It is striking that the five computer-generated planetary systems show a distribution of rocky planets and gas giants similar to that of the Solar System. But if the computer is fed with present-day astronomical theory, this is the sort of result that one would expect. Given that the parent stars of these planetary systems are carbon copies of the Sun, then 'planet two' from System number 141 looks the most promising for the origin and evolution of life. 'Planet four' in System 147 is the right distance from its sun, though less massive, and may also be suitable.

The Solar System is shown here for comparison.

planets of other stars, but they are asking too much. At their nearest, such planets would be several light-years away. They would be small dim objects relatively close to large bright objects, which are the stars they orbit. Even a dim star could be thousands of times brighter than its planets.

Such great differences in luminosity make the separation of a planet from its star a major observational problem. From a distance of several light-years a planet will appear very close to its star. Planet seekers have to be ready to cope with a probable separation equal only to 1/10,000 the diameter of the Moon as observed from Earth.

Thus, the ideal planet for detection would be large, perhaps several times the size of Jupiter, with an orbit the greatest possible distance from its star which should be as dim as possible. A detectable planet might also have its own internal energy source (like Jupiter and Saturn). Then it would radiate more energy than it received from its star, thereby increasing the amount of observable radiation.

Ground based astronomy may never be able to detect small rocky planets like the Earth. Our atmosphere greatly weakens and randomises much of the information received from the universe and prevents the necessary observational precision. Only Jupiter-sized bodies (or larger) may be detectable from the Earth's surface, and astronomers will only detect planets like ours by the use of telescopes in space. Yet even from that perfect viewpoint it will not be easy, and the initial searches will be for large planets.

So far, the most encouraging discoveries have come from observing in infrared radiation. Astronomers point out that visible light is not the best part of the electromagnetic spectrum in which to detect the planets of other stars. A planet re-radiates in the infrared much of the energy it receives from its star and can be 1,000 times brighter in infrared than in visible light.

In 1983 the Infrared Astronomical Satellite (IRAS) detected excessive infrared radiation from several dozen stars, in particular Vega, Formulhaut and Beta Pictoris (see colour section). The infrared was intense and scientists guessed that these stars must have orbiting discs of dust and debris to provide large radiating areas. If this material had already formed into planet-sized bodies, the surface area radiating infrared would have been reduced so greatly that the level of radiation would not have been detectable by IRAS.

By chance, two American astronomers, Dr Rich Terrile and Dr Brad Smith, were carrying out an observing program at the Las Campañas Observatory in Chile when they read a report of the IRAS discoveries. They happened to be in exactly the right place to photograph the star Beta Pictoris, which is 50 light-years away. Using a coronograph (an instrument designed to observe faint rings or nebulae around bright objects), Terrile and Smith obtained the most spectacular supporting evidence yet for the existence of other planetary systems. Beta Pictoris, they discovered, has a great disc of matter in orbit, 20 times the diameter of the Solar System (see colour section). Its existence supports current theories which accept that planets form within a stellar disc of gas and debris. But no habitable planets will ever orbit Beta Pictoris, a young star (more massive and seven times more luminous than the Sun) because of its intense radiation.

Another method of searching for extrasolar planets has been developed by Dr Don McCarthy and colleagues at the University of Arizona. They call it 'Near-Infrared Speckle Interferometry'. Put briefly, McCarthy takes several thousand frames (photographing at 100 frames a second) of a star suspected of having a large planet. This brief exposure time 'freezes' the many speckles of light which normally make up the star's image. The 'speckles' are produced by turbulence in the atmosphere, and each 'frozen' speckle contains an image undistorted by atmospheric movement. When all the information from the several thousand frames is processed one clear picture is produced.

In theory, McCarthy's technique can detect a planet where its star is up to 100 times more luminous than the planet – and that is a very dim star indeed. Therefore, it may be possible to detect Jupiter-sized planets from ground-based observatories; but when operating in space the system may be able to detect Earth-sized planets, although it will be difficult.

It could be that the Hubble Space Telescope will make the first observations of extrasolar planets, providing they are the size of Jupiter or larger and orbiting the nearest stars. The Hubble Telescope is the most advanced telescope ever built, and from orbit its 94-inch mirror will see the universe in a *thousand* times more detail than any previous instrument.

According to accepted astronomical theory, there is a clear distinction between star formation and planet formation – although, so far as mass is concerned, there may be almost a continuous scale from planets to the dimmest of stars. Planets are formed by the accretion (coming together) of dust and debris into increasingly larger bodies. In contrast, stars are formed from gas clouds which collapse and contract under their own gravity until matter becomes so dense and hot that nuclear fusion begins, and the star starts to shine.

WOBBLING IN SPACE

At one time there was generally accepted evidence that certain stars wobble due to the presence of large planets. Dr Peter van de Kamp, a pioneer in the search for extrasolar planets, had collected evidence over a period of 40 years at the Sproul Observatory of Swarthmore College, Pennsylvania.

His research was exacting and time-consuming in the extreme. He once explained the problem like this:

All stars are moving around the Galaxy at different speeds, like cars on a giant racetrack. The *proper motion* [observed movement] of a single star should be in a straight line, but the presence of unseen companions around a star will unbalance its motion, so that its path appears to wobble.

Van de Kamp and his colleagues routinely recorded the apparent wobbles of 20 neighbouring stars, and it was thought that some of these wobbles were caused by very large planets. Sadly, however, a major fault was detected in the telescope and all the early results had to be disregarded. Van de Kamp (who always emphasised the possibility of observational errors) continued his research until 1976, but no one has been able to confirm his claimed detections of several massive planets.

The fact that observations have to be made beneath the atmosphere tends to swamp the evidence, but the attempt to detect planets indirectly by wobbles in the movements of stars is a sound technique and new projects with improved instrumentation are under way.

The University of Arizona and NASA will put the Astrometric Telescope Facility (an infrared telescope with a

1.25-metre mirror) into orbit in the mid-1990s. It will be fixed to NASA's Space Station (see colour section) after being used at the Mauna Kea Observatory in Hawaii which is situated at a height of 4,200 metres above sea level, well above most of the atmosphere.

The telescope will measure stellar wobbles, and when in space may be able to detect Earth-sized planets orbiting stars within 30 light-years of the Sun, and Jupiter-sized planets out to 100 light-years. But George Gatewood, Director of the Allegheny Observatory in Pittsburgh, who planned the Astrometric Telescope Facility, anticipates that it may take up to a couple of decades to accumulate acceptable evidence of the planets of neighbouring stars.

Dr Gatewood has developed a new technique for detecting stellar wobbles which goes by the name of 'MAP' (multi-channel astrometric photometry). It records star positions accurately and quickly and will be used with the Astrometric Telescope Facility on the Space Station.

MAP consists of fibre optics, computers and other electronic technology currently used in astronomy, plus a transparent plate which is crossed by many parellel black lines (four pairs of lines to the millimetre). The plate moves at a known rate. As the lines cross the frame, they modulate the light from the stars within the field of view. This includes the 'target' star and distant 'fixed' stars used for reference purposes. From the known rate of movement of the plate and the light received through it, the position of the target star can be recorded accurately. Wobbles in star movement, due to the presence of large planets, can be measured far more quickly by Gatewood's technique than by classical methods.

Numerous groups of astronomers are developing different techniques for the indirect detection of other planetary systems, greatly encouraged by the growing capacity of space technology to locate their equipment above our obscuring atmosphere.

TELL-TALE LINES

For more than 100 years astronomers have used spectroscopes to study the spectral lines in the light from stars. Each element has its own specific set of lines which tell us what the stars are made of. The lines show as bright emission lines or as dark

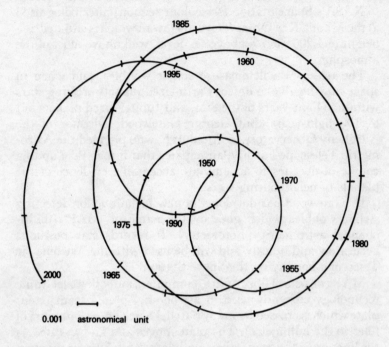

This plot by Roger Sinnott shows the orbit of the Sun around the centre of mass of the Solar System from 1950 to the year 2000. The large loops, each averaging a dozen years, are caused mainly by our most massive planets Jupiter and Saturn. It represents what alien astronomers could observe of the Sun from a distance of six light-years (from Barnard's star). We assume they have a telescope like the 30-inch instrument at Dr Gatewood's Observatory at Allegheny. They would see the Sun as a star with apparent magnitude of +1.1; but our largest planet, Jupiter, would not be visible because the Sun is 250 million times brighter. Yet the effect of Jupiter's gravitational pull on the Sun would be detectable. It would pull the Sun away from its average path through space by as much as 0.003 arc second. A cycle would be repeated about every 12 years.

absorption lines where the star's radiation is absorbed at certain wavelengths by elements in its outer layers (see colour section).

But these lines can also be used to measure a star's velocity. The lines are shifted to the red when the star recedes (the well-known 'red-shift' or Doppler effect) or to the violet end of the spectrum when it moves towards us. Astronomers have applied this fact (to take one example) to study close pairs of stars (binary stars) which orbit each other. Sometimes a faint companion star has not been detected visually; so close together are the two stars that they shine as one. Only shifts in the spectral lines have shown the presence of two stars and have provided data on the mass and orbit of the unseen companion. In theory, the same method could detect planets.

Let's take our nearest star, the Sun, to illustrate the problem. Jupiter's gravitational effect changes the Sun's velocity by up to 13 metres per second, and produces detectable shifts in the Sun's spectral lines. The Earth's effect on the Sun is minute – it changes the Sun's velocity by only 0.1 metre per second. An alien astronomer some light-years away might detect the presence of Jupiter by the periodic shifts in the Sun's spectrum. The other gas giants (Saturn, Uranus and Neptune) would also cause changes in the Sun's velocity. After many years observing the Sun, the alien astronomer would discover a definite pattern in the way the lines in its spectrum shifted, first one way then the other. The pattern would be repeated indefinitely. And from this pattern the alien observer would, in theory, be able to work out the masses of our major planets and the dimensions of their orbits. That is how some planet seekers on Earth are trying to detect the planets of other stars.

Astronomers have routinely measured these changes in velocity to within 50 metres per second. But the latest equipment can measure velocities down to 1 metre per second.

Dr Bill Cochran, who has developed such equipment at the University of Texas, hopes to detect Jupiter-sized planets from his ground-based observatory. The shifting spectral lines can be recorded almost as well from beneath the atmosphere as from above it. It's the only planet-seeking technique that doesn't work much better from space. The other advantages are that the close proximity of a planet to its star does not affect its detectability. And to a certain extent, the distance of the target star is no obtacle to observations, providing the star's level of radiation is adequate.

Another way to detect planets is to record the minute changes in light intensity from a star when planets move across its image. The problem is that stellar eruptions, like sunspots on the Sun, may produce minute changes in luminosity. But several groups of astronomers are investigating this way of detecting planets.

Perhaps the most ambitious planet seekers work at the University of Arizona, where Dr Roger Angel and others are planning a future infrared space telescope with a 16-metre diameter mirror – a very costly venture. Indeed, in view of the cost, it could remain on the drawing-board for years. But eventually it may be used to search for the spectral lines of oxygen in the infrared coming from neighbouring stars, signalling the existence of Earth-like planets. Such a telescope, besides being a wonderful instrument for astronomy in general, would provide instant information. The detection of the spectral lines of oxygen would not only indicate the presence of planets, but also the presence of life. We would not have to wait a decade or two to measure the wobbles of stars which, even then, could only indicate the presence of planets and not the presence of life on those planets, which is our ultimate concern.

OTHER PLANETARY SYSTEMS

But apart from any thoughts of ETIs, the search for other planetary systems is important to astronomy. The formation of planetary systems is probably part of star formation – at least in the formation of single stars. Multiple star systems (and the majority of stars belong to such systems) may also have planets, though perhaps seldom habitable planets. With two or three stars in a stellar system, planetary orbits could be rather eccentric. If some neighbouring stars do not possess planets, just orbiting discs of debris instead, then astronomers will have to revise their theories about the origin of the Solar System.

We can imagine numerous scenarios for other planetary systems, and we could say that the one in which the Solar System is average has the highest probability of being true. Once again, it's the application of the old principle of mediocrity which is often justified – though not always. We must

View from a planet orbiting Alpha Centauri A. This star system contains the three nearest stars to the Earth: Alpha Centauri A is a yellow star similar to the Sun; Alpha Centauri B a smaller and orange sun; Proxima Centauri a dim red star at a great distance from the planet.

The distance between Alpha Centauri A and B is 25 times the Earth–Sun distance, a large enough separation to allow habitable planets to orbit either A or B, though the latter may be too small a star to have a continuously habitable zone for any planet.

remember that the Earth is only a tiny part of the Solar System, and for this reason we have to be cautious. Although there are no reasons for thinking that our G2 type star (the Sun) is different from the millions of other G2 stars in the Galaxy, it could be that only a very small proportion have planets like Earth, planets with the right mass, gravity and orbits for the origin and evolution of life.

Mere minor differences in the way the Solar System formed could have made the evolution of an inhabited Earth impossible. Planetary systems that are almost identical to ours may exist in abundance – our system may be average in that sense – but the evolution of planets like the Earth where life can flourish for billions of years may be very rare. Yet where such planets do exist, life and intelligence may also exist, as we know from our own experience.

One of the many extraterrestrials created by artists. These two harmless-looking creatures are supposed to have evolved on a water-covered planet that is otherwise Earth-like. Apparently, they are living in a substantial structure, yet they show no signs whatever of having any means of constructing anything. Also a water-covered planet does not seem a promising habitat for the evolution of builders and technologists when we look at life in our own oceans. Biologically credible ETIs are hard to find in art, fiction and films.

LIFE AND ATMOSPHERES

The evolution of the Earth's atmosphere and the evolution of life have been inseparable, the one continually affecting the development of the other. Life and the atmosphere, the Earth's land surface and oceans are all one system. We are beginning to appreciate that for such a system to develop for four billion years, as it has here, planets would have to orbit stars of about the same mass as the Sun. And planets with advanced lifeforms may have masses similar to that of the Earth, whilst their orbits may fall within an extremely narrow zone. Outside of that narrow zone they may not remain continuously habitable, although many may have life which evolves for millions of years. It could be that Mars may one day illustrate this point for us, if we should find there, in ancient sedimentary rocks, fossilised microbes that became extinct some three billion years ago.

Until the early 1970s it was widely accepted that an atmosphere for the origin and evolution of life progressed from one rich in basic hydrogen compounds to its chemical opposite, an atmosphere with abundant oxygen. Laboratory experiments by numerous scientists had shown that a hydrogen-dominated atmosphere promotes for the formation of the basic molecules of life. Many of these molecules form automatically in an atmosphere of hydrogen compounds when energy is injected. That energy can be electricity, heat or radiation. But similar experiments using an oxygen atmosphere, which is necessary for the evolution of more advanced and active life, produce none of the molecular units of life one with free oxygen. Life, it seems, cannot form in an oxidising atmosphere, although it needs that atmosphere later for higher forms of life.

Scientists concluded long ago that hydrogen and helium, the lightest and most abundant elements, were driven from the Earth as it formed by solar radiation; that the first atmosphere came from the primordial Earth's hot interior – from intense volcanic activity. The question is how much hydrogen degassed in this way? Most geologists now think that the Earth's first atmosphere was composed of carbon dioxide, nitrogen and water vapour; that it was not the hydrogen-dominated atmosphere once assumed. Nevertheless, it's reasonable to accept that enough hydrogen and its com-

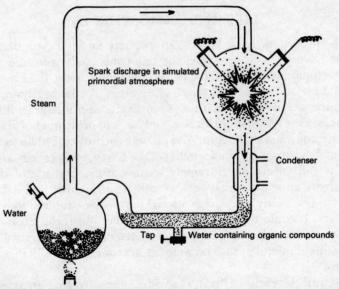

Spark discharge in simulated primordial atmosphere

Steam

Condenser

Water

Tap — Water containing organic compounds

(a) Dr Stanley Miller's classic experiment in 1953 on the origin of life was based on the assumption that the Earth's primordial atmosphere was composed of hydrogen and hydrogen compounds, such as methane and ammonia – the kind of atmosphere possessed by Jupiter. When such an atmosphere is simulated in the laboratory (in a closed system) and is subjected to energy of some kind, many of the building blocks of life form automatically. Since 1953 Miller's experiment has been repeated many times, using various forms of energy (ultraviolet light, radioactivity, heat and so on). All produced similar results.

However, we now have a problem. It looks as if the primordial Earth did *not* have a hydrogen-dominated atmosphere of the kind assumed by Miller and those who repeated his experiment with such success. It now looks as if the Earth's first real atmosphere was composed mainly of carbon dioxide and nitrogen. As the Earth formed, the hydrogen and helium were driven off by the Sun's heat, leaving the heavier elements behind. Only relatively small quantities of the light elements remained. Nevertheless, on the primordial Earth there may have existed places where enough hydrogen compounds remained to provide the sort of conditions simulated by Miller. Certainly, the energy sources used in his (and later) experiments, were constantly available on the young Earth.

(b) Possible sources of energy for the origin of life.

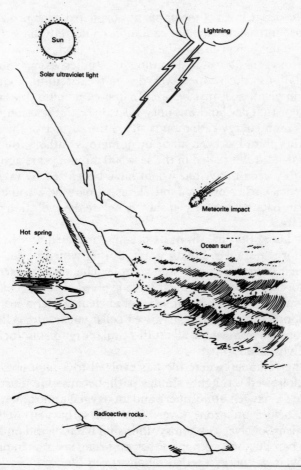

pounds existed in the atmosphere to justify the many experiments on primordial atmospheres that have shown how the molecular units of life could have been formed.

Later, photosynthesising organisms would have to evolve to provide an oxygen atmosphere which makes possible the evolution of more advanced life. On Earth it was photosynthesising bacteria (sometimes misleadingly called blue–green algae) which put oxygen into the atmosphere for a couple of billion years before higher forms of plant life began to evolve.

The Earth's atmosphere has served to prevent the escape of volatile molecules like water, and has provided a protective shield against radiation and high energy particles. In particular, the ozone layer of the upper atmosphere which protects life against intense ultraviolet radiation could only have formed when enough oxygen became available. (Ozone is a molecule of three oxygen atoms.) According to studies using computer simulations, the ozone layer did not exist until about 500 million years ago, just before life first came onto dry land. It could be that dry land was not a tolerable habitat as long as the Sun's high energy radiation reached the surface of the Earth, and this point has been made by numerous authors. But of the animals that flourished in the seas 500 million years ago, there probably aren't any that would have benefitted by taking up residence earlier on dry land. Thus, it may be a coincidence that the ozone layer formed shortly before the evolution of land animals.

We know that life, from its origin, continued at a bacterial level for some three billion years, during which period many different living structures and complex chemistries, used later by more advanced life, must have evolved. It now looks as if the coming together (symbiosis) of ancient bacteria led to the development of the first advanced cells (eucaryotic cells), the kind of cells from which all multi-cellular organisms, including ourselves, are formed.

Other planets, where life has evolved to a high level, may have followed a roughly similar path, because life must come before an oxygen atmosphere and an oxygen atmosphere must come before an ozone layer. And unless oxygen-producing organisms evolve, as photosynthesising bacteria did on Earth, there can be no oxygen for either an ozone layer or to provide the levels of energy needed by advanced life.

THE STRUCTURE OF EVOLUTION

It is now known that photosynthesising bacteria existed 3.5 billion years ago. In 1986 researchers at the University of California, led by Professor J. William Schopf, announced the discovery of fossils of oxygen-producing bacteria (the biological term is cyanobacteria) in rocks found near Port Hedland in Western Australia (see colour section).

There is also abundant evidence of life, identified as bacteria, which exists in rocks elsewhere and that dates back to 3.5 billion years ago. The earliest evidence of life, in the form of

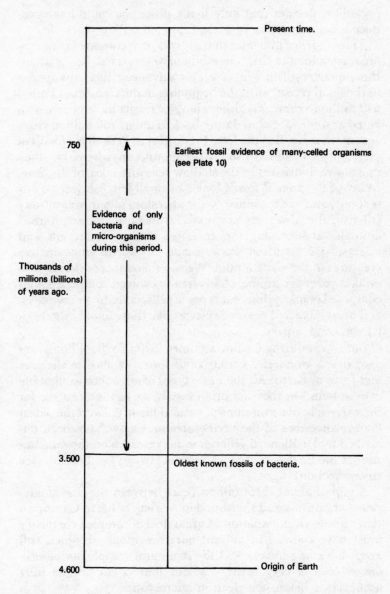

Present time.

750 — Earliest fossil evidence of many-celled organisms
(see Plate 10)

Evidence of only
bacteria and
micro-organisms
during this period.

Thousands of
millions (billions)
of years ago.

3.500 — Oldest known fossils of bacteria.

4.600 — Origin of Earth

Why did it take so long for life to progress from single-celled microbes to the first many-celled organisms? That gap of almost three billion years, when apparently nothing but single-celled organisms existed on Earth, presents quite a puzzle.

organic molecules that only living processes could have produced, actually exists in rocks some 3.8 billion years old.

This evidence indicates that life on Earth consisted of microorganisms for the first three billion years. That is, for about three-quarters of life's history. Few 'advanced' lifeforms appear in the fossil record until the beginning of the Cambrian Period 570 million years ago, although older fossils have been discovered at some rare sites dating back to about 750 million years ago, in what is called the Late Precambrian Period. No fossils of plants of this age have so far been found anywhere, but they must have flourished in the shallow seas and lakes of the time. Many of the animal fossils look like small jellyfish (see colour section), and are presumably the ancestors of our present-day jellyfish. But also there are small fossils of the jointed-limbed animals (arthropods), the ancestors of the crustaceans and insects, and fossilised tracks made by worms and sluglike creatures in the ancient mud. We can therefore see that by 750 million years ago animals had already evolved complex bodies composed of many different types of cells, including nerve cells, and must have had nervous systems like those found in today's jellyfish and worms.

But it was during Cambrian times (570 to 500 million years ago) that a wonderful variety of lifeforms evolved in the seas and lakes of Earth. All the basic types of advanced animal life can be found in the Cambrian fossils, as anyone can see for themselves in our museums of natural history. Even the oldest known ancestors of the vertebrates may now have been described by Dr Richard Jefferies in his research on the *calcichordates* at the British Museum (Natural History) in London (see colour section).

A gap of about three billion years between the first single-celled organisms and the abundant variety of life in Cambrian times needs an explanation. A great deal of complex chemistry must have evolved in ancient bacteria, much of which still keeps life going today. And the structural complexity of advanced cells is very great – a fact that could not be fully appreciated before the electron microscope.

We are only just beginning to appreciate the significance of this pattern of evolution on Earth. And it suggests the possibility that there may have been a parallel development of microbial life on Mars in the early days, until an irreversible ice age took over the planet a few billion years ago. From studies of the Martian surface and theoretical studies of the evolution of planetary atmospheres, there are reasons for thinking that Mars may have initially followed a somewhat similar pattern of development to Earth, and that micro-organisms evolved and flourished while there was liquid water on the planet (see

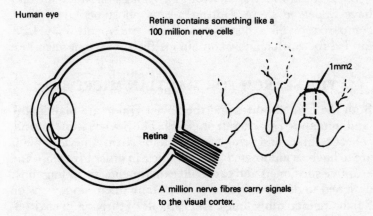

Human eye

Retina contains something like a 100 million nerve cells

1mm2

Retina

A million nerve fibres carry signals to the visual cortex.

Nerve cells have become well organised since the first known animals evolved, such as the medusoid shown in Plate 10. By about 700 million years ago, that animal and its many relatives must have had a nervous system like that of a present-day jellyfish, which manages to function very well with a simple network of nerve cells. But jellyfish have no eyes or advanced sensory systems.

Today, when we consider the complexity of our own nervous system we can only marvel at the achievement of evolution. The eye, our most important sense organ, has something like 100 million nerve cells in the retina. And our retinas receive information by light which is then carried by a million nerve fibres to the visual cortex of the brain. The cortex, the folded layer overlaying the rest of the brain, is the most recent neural structure to evolve. In human beings and dolphins, it is tightly folded to pack a large sheet of nerve cells within a reasonably sized skull. (See Plates 4 and 5.)

The small section of the human cortex (*top*) is only 2 mm thick, but below every square millimetre exist some 100,000 nerve cells, each one having many connections to other cells. The total number of nerve cells within the cortex is about ten billion, with something like a hundred times this number of connections.

47

colour section). There would have been no need of oxygen in the Martian atmosphere. There was no free oxygen in the primordial atmosphere of the Earth. Indeed, when the first photosynthesising bacteria began to put oxygen into the atmosphere, as a waste product of their photosynthesising metabolism, it was a gas toxic to other micro-organisms.

So, if liquid water existed for long enough on Mars, life may have appeared there. During a very short period of time, compared to life's history on Earth, sediments may have formed rocks which now contain fossilised Martian microbes.

THE SEARCH FOR MARTIAN MICROBES

Both the United States and the Soviet Union are planning to land unmanned spacecraft on Mars. The Soviets want to land, collect samples and bring them back to Earth. American plans are to have an automated 'rover' vehicle in order to explore and examine specimens and carry out experiments, including those designed to detect evidence of life. Many micro-organisms on Earth are incredibly tough and capable of thriving in environments that would immediately kill other living things. They may have become even tougher on Mars, in which case it is just possible that some are still living there in very restricted habitats. But this doesn't seem likely. Fossil microbes are perhaps the best we can hope for. The two Viking Landers, thousands of miles apart, found oxidising chemicals on the Martian surface powerful enough to destroy all organic molecules. Indeed, no organic molecules of any kind were detected on Mars. Also, intense ultraviolet radiation that breaks up organic molecules strikes the surface of Mars, which is unprotected by its rarified atmosphere. So low is the atmospheric pressure that thin layers of frost, photographed on Mars by the Viking Landers, must simply vaporise on heating.

But we should not completely rule out the possibility of finding evidence of life on Mars, even though that life might have died out aeons ago. Certainly, a thorough search for it will be made because the fact that life had formed on two neighbouring worlds so soon after their formation would confirm that life is a universal phenomenon. And one of humanity's major questions would at last be answered.

The pattern of evolution on Earth, the initial stage of which may have been repeated on Mars, may be the only way to advanced life: a few billion years of evolving micro-organisms to establish environmental conditions and advanced cells for higher life to form, followed by rapid evolution of a vast variety of lifeforms.

STABLE STARS

Yet creatures capable of developing technology could only evolve where their star (sun) remains stable for several billions of years. A star's stable period, when energy comes from the 'burning' of hydrogen to form helium, is the main part of its life cycle. We know that the more massive a star is the quicker it consumes its hydrogen in this way and leaves its stable period. We also know that it does so at a rate roughly equal to the cube of the star's mass (m^3) in stars that are more than three times the mass of the Sun. Thus a star that is ten times more massive than the Sun 'burns' its hydrogen to helium and passes through its stable period a thousand (10^3) times faster than a star like the Sun. It will remain stable for only ten million years compared with the ten *billion* years calculated for the Sun. A star just twice the Sun's mass uses up its hydrogen at an even higher rate $(m^{4.5})$ and goes through its stable period 22.4 times $(2^{4.5})$ as quickly. Therefore, no chance for technological intelligence to evolve on planets belonging to stars like these, when differences in the mass of stars so greatly affects the time during which they could support habitable planets. Even a star just 25 per cent more massive than the Sun would end its stable period at about the same age as the Sun is today.

The stable periods of stars range from a few million years for O-type stars, the most massive and brightest stars, to many billions of years for M-type stars, the least massive and least luminous. The Sun, a G2 star, has already passed through half its stable period, but the stable period of an M-type star will be more than the present age of the Galaxy.

Because of the historical development of astronomical nomenclature, stars are now classified O,B,A,F,G,K,M. O-type stars are the most massive; M-type stars the least massive. After M there used to be R,N and S-type stars, classifications now discarded. The old mnemonic for star classification used to be 'O, be a fine girl kiss me right now sweetie', but this no longer requires the last three words.

Although we call the Sun an average star, more than 85 per cent of stars are less massive and less luminous, which means they will remain stable stars for longer. But only a small proportion of these stars may have habitable planets. To begin with, more than 75 per cent of all stars are part of double or multiple star systems. There may be planets in such systems, as has been mentioned earlier, but their orbits might make them unsuitable for life. It depends on how close to each other are the stars of double or multiple systems. Planets with stable biospheres should be possible in double systems where the two stars are very close to each other, so that a family of planets could orbit the two stars as if they were one.

We can see how habitable planets may be possible in a double system where the two stars are well separated by looking at Jupiter and the Sun. Jupiter is 320 times the mass of the Earth and 2.5 times the mass of all the other bodies of the Solar System combined, excluding the Sun. And Jupiter has what amounts to a planetary system of its own in its family of moons. (The same can be said for the other gas giants.)

Had Jupiter been about 50 times more massive the hydrogen at its core would have become hot enough to start nuclear fusion. Jupiter would then have been a red dwarf star, like the many red dwarfs in the neighbourhood of the Sun. Had such a small, dim star existed instead of Jupiter it would most probably not have affected the evolution of life on Earth. But the presence of massive stars in double and multiple systems would not favour the evolution of habitable planets. Stars several times more massive than the Sun would end their stable periods in nuclear outbursts of inconceivable magnitude which would surely end the habitability of any planets.

With stars of the Sun's mass (and less) the prospects for habitable planets in double and multiple systems seem better. Dr Robert Harrington of the US Naval Observatory, Washington DC, calculated in a computer study that the orbits of planets in double star systems could be very stable. Harrington then tested his results on the Solar System. He replaced the Sun by two stars, each half the mass of the Sun and separated by 0.4 astronomical units and an eccentricity in their orbits of 0.5. (An astronomical unit is the average Earth–Sun distance.) Mercury, the nearest planet to the change, was very upset and soon left the Solar System, whilst Venus changed its orbit slightly. But all the other planets continued as they are.

Harrington also replaced Jupiter with a star of the same mass as the Sun in order to discover the effect on the inner planets. Again, it was only the closest planet to the change, Mars, which suffered. In fact, Mars behaved very badly; its orbit became unstable and it looked as if it would eventually leave the system. But the other inner planets remained in their present orbits.

Nevertheless, the radiation from another sun at the distance of Jupiter would surely have affected the evolution of life, even if its gravitational influence on the Earth's orbit was insignificant. For example, life's adaptations to light may have been different. And the extra radiation may have affected the evolution of the Earth's atmosphere and climate.

NARROW ESCAPES FOR EARTH

The evolution of atmospheres and habitable planets now seems rather more complicated than was previously supposed. Dr Michael Hart, when at NASA's Goddard Space Flight Center, showed in theory just how precariously balanced may be the physical conditions on which the Earth's development rests. Indeed, it almost did not become a habitable world at all, narrowly escaping catastrophy on two occasions.

Hart ran a computer program, working through dozens of different Earth histories, starting each with a different set of conditions to find which set best fitted what we know of Earth history and present conditions. The Earth's age in the study was 4.6 billion years – the age which geologists and astronomers now accept as established by radioactive dating techniques, using Earth and Moon rocks and meteorites.

The study showed that within the first 150 million years of Earth history, water clouds completely covered our planet. These clouds existed in an atmosphere 1.5 times denser than today's, and by 3.5 billion years ago the Earth's temperature had reached a critical point. As on Venus, where an atmosphere about 100 times denser than ours keeps the planet's surface several times hotter than boiling water, the primordial atmosphere of Earth stopped heat from the Sun being radiated back into space. Hart found at this stage that the Earth almost turned into a second Venus. He wrote: 'Had the Earth been slightly closer to the Sun a runaway greenhouse effect would have occurred fairly early in the Earth's history.'

The Earth was saved by the first photosynthesising bacteria (blue-green algae or, more precisely, cyanobacteria). These micro-organisms, which must have evolved from earlier bacteria, possessed the first chemical machinery for synthesising the molecules they needed for growth (their equivalent of food) by using sunlight as their energy source for the process. Like the plant life which later evolved from these microbes, simple inorganic chemicals and sunlight were all they needed.

As photosynthesising bacteria used up the carbon dioxide in the atmosphere to make organic molecules for their growth and reproduction, the effectiveness of the heat trap and the Earth's temperature decreased. By 2.75 billion years ago, the clouds had broken up and the atmosphere was just half its present density. By two billion years ago photosynthesising organisms had released so much oxygen that the atmosphere began to oxidise rocks for the first time. The familiar red deposits of iron oxide are one example. But then, with less atmosphere to retain the Sun's heat, the Earth began to cool. Within 500,000 years, ice sheets covered 10 per cent of an Earth heading towards an irreversible ice age.

'Had the Earth's orbit been slightly larger', Hart wrote, 'then runaway glaciation would have occurred about two billion years ago.' The study showed that an increase of the Earth–Sun distance by just 1 per cent would have been enough, and that the Earth came within 1°C of becoming permanently frozen. Hart's results therefore predict that Mars, which is further from the Sun, should have long ago experienced this runaway glaciation. And, indeed, the investigations of Mars have shown the existence of a permanent ice age there, though there may be little water-ice now left on the planet.

Not until 420 million years ago, according to the study, was there enough oxygen and ozone (composed of three oxygen atoms) in the Earth's atmosphere to shield dry land from the Sun's high energy radiation and allow life to leave the protection of water for the first time. As we know, land plants established themselves first, then invertebrate animals. Later the fishes – a group of lung fish – came onto the muddy borders of lakes and rivers and evolved into the first amphibians some 350 million years ago.

So, do the majority of potential Earths, orbiting stars like the Sun, get caught by one of the two runaway processes, becoming permanently frozen worlds like Mars or planetary furnaces like Venus? It's a question Hart's work provokes. The idea that, for the origin and evolution of life, a planet had only to occupy an orbit around its star, the so-called *habitable zone*, where the temperature range enabled water to be liquid, now looks too simple.

NO HIGH GRAVITY TECHNOLOGISTS

Theory indicates that planets for advanced life must also have a mass within a limited range. The science fiction idea of highly intelligent creatures as flat as pancakes, living on a planet with several times the gravity of Earth, looks biologically and astronomically impossible. Active creatures of the kind that might eventually evolve into technologists would need an atmosphere with plenty of oxygen to obtain their energy; and planets much more massive than the Earth could not evolve such an atmosphere. Research results indicate that a planet, which orbits in a potentially continuously habitable zone, must have a radius and mass within a certain range to avoid either the greenhouse effect or permanent glaciation. To support life for several billion years (like the Earth), and evolve an oxygen-rich atmosphere, a planet cannot have a gravity much less than 10 per cent of 1g or much greater than 20 per cent.

We might even ask the question 'Can rocky planets far more massive than the Earth form around stars like the Sun?' Of course we cannot know how often sufficient quantities of heavy elements are present around young stars to form really gigantic rocky planets. But we can note that within the Solar System the Earth is the largest rocky planet, and that the gas giants are much more massive only because they formed at a greater distance from the heat of the Sun and therefore could retain so much hydrogen and helium. The Earth, situated relatively close to the Sun, easily lost these light elements. It is interesting to note that the gas giant Saturn would be about the same mass as the Earth if its atmosphere were stripped away to the rocky core.

STARS FOR EARTH-LIKE PLANETS

For many years, it was thought that F, G and K stars could all possess habitable planets – even stars of low mass and luminosity such as the M-type stars. Each class of star, by the way, is subdivided into ten, so that there are, for example, G-type stars from G0 to G9; the lower the number the more massive and luminous the star (see colour section 24).

The habitable zone for planets, so it was supposed, would be broader and more distant for F-type stars and nearer and narrower around the less luminous M-type stars. As we have just mentioned, this was too simple a view. According to Hart's second computer study, the continuously habitable zone becomes narrower as stars become less massive, and no longer exists with stars which have a mass of just 83 per cent that of the Sun or less. That is, in typical K1 stars. This means that the vast majority of stars less massive than the Sun can have no continuously habitable planets.

Hart's study also shows that stars just 10 per cent more massive than the Sun will emit too much ultraviolet radiation after four billion years for life to be able to establish itself on land. So had the Sun been 10 per cent more massive there would have been no land life on Earth. And potentially habitable planets with suns 20 per cent more massive than the Sun will become too hot for life. Almost all planets may, therefore, become either too hot or too cold before intelligent life has time to evolve. Only a small percentage of planets, which have suns whose mass is within about 10 per cent of the Sun's mass, have a chance of becoming Earth-like. And then only a chance, for they must have appropriate mass and also be within a rather narrow orbital zone. Otherwise, they cannot evolve an Earth-like atmosphere and provide a continuously habitable home for life. So it seems that planets for intelligent life, whose hypothetical abundance has so often been proclaimed, may not be abundant after all.

This conclusion is pessimistic compared with many previous estimates on the numbers of habitable planets, but it is probably better for future thinking on our subject to be pessimistic rather than optimistic. Estimates of extraterrestrial life and habitable planets have, in the past, been calculated logically from certain assumptions. But years ago, the American astronomer Luyten cautioned us about this by quoting Kettering's remark that 'Logic is an organised way of going wrong with confidence.'

Anyway, if advances in space technology lead to the colonisation of lifeless planets and moons, the abundance or otherwise of worlds like the Earth may be irrelevant; that is to say, as far as the possible number of civilisations in the Galaxy is concerned. One civilisation on an Earth-like planet could have established itself on thousands of other worlds. Given that intelligent beings can be transported in some way across interstellar space, then colonisation may be the overriding factor in establishing civilisations throughout the billions of galaxies in the observable universe.

EXOTIC HABITATS FOR LIFE

So far, in our speculations on sites for life, we have been concerned with rocky planets, worlds with solid surfaces. But there are the gas giants as well; these are a very different type of planet which retain a primordial atmosphere and have no planetary surface. And we may ask ourselves if gas giants could provide a niche for life, though not perhaps for technological life. Could these two distinct types of planet, one wonders, provide two distinct types of environment for life throughout the universe? According to astronomical theory, other planetary systems should include both gas giants and rocky planets.

Before dealing with the gas giants themselves, we had better consider a couple of their exotic moons: Europa and Titan which are comparable in size to our own Moon. Jupiter's second major moon, Europa, appears to be completely covered by badly cracked ice. And beneath the ice there may be a warm ocean, according to evidence provided by Voyager 2. This is possible because the inside of Europa is subjected to the powerful gravitational fields of Jupiter and its neighbouring moons Io and Ganymede. These gravitational fields so severely affect Io's interior that the energy generated is released in a continuous series of volcanic eruptions. The heat produced in Europa is insufficient for this, but it might maintain a warm ocean under the moon's thick crust of ice.

Saturn's largest moon, Titan, is a very different world. An orange atmosphere of methane-ice, nitrogen and organic molecules, 1.5 times the density of our atmosphere, may hide a sea of methane and ethane one kilometre deep. And beneath this exotic sea, which probably covers Titan, there may be a crust of water-ice crystals and organic materials. Titan is a very cold world – the sunlight falling there is only one hundredth of that which falls on Earth – but it will be a fascinating place for organic chemists and is sure to be well studied by space probes in the future.

An intimate study of the Solar System's gas giants may just possibly provide a way, this side of the stars, of studying life as a universal phenomenon. The atmosphere of Jupiter appears primordial, unchanged since the formation of the Solar System. That of Saturn is similar. And Uranus and Neptune, smaller and further from the Sun, can have changed little since their formation.

Although the gas giants have no surface, apart from their cloud tops, there may be layers in their atmospheres where pressures and temperatures produce ocean-like environments. The deeper a layer is in the atmosphere the hotter it is. So that where a water layer coincides with the right pressure and temperature range, there could exist 'atmospheric oceans' for organic chemistry. Such oceans in gas giants would be thousands of times larger in volume than the seas of the primordial Earth. There is indirect evidence from the Voyager flypast that a layer of hot water exists some 5,000 miles beneath the surface clouds of Uranus. The main source of this water is thought to be comets – comets having been described as 'dirty snowballs'. Both Uranus and Neptune are more vulnerable to collisions with comets than Earth because of their high gravitational attraction, and because they are nearer to the source of comets at the boundary of the Solar System.

Jupiter and Saturn are hotter than Uranus, though they receive little heat from the Sun. Both radiate internal heat which has been explained provisionally by very slow gravitational contraction. Nevertheless, Jupiter and Saturn do appear to offer the opportunity to see the results of more than four billion years of organic chemistry. Laboratory experiments on primordial atmospheres during the past 30 years have produced the molecules of life in abundance with colours that match the brownish reds of Jupiter and Saturn.

Unfortunately, the build-up of organic molecules to that

point where life could form may have been prevented on Jupiter and Saturn because their internal heat must create powerful convection currents. Jupiter radiates about three times as much heat as it receives from the Sun; Saturn about twice as much. The signs of the convection currents produced by this heat are obvious in NASA's photographs of Jupiter and Saturn. Any organic molecules building up in complexity towards life would therefore be carried upwards to lower temperatures and pressures and then downwards to certain incineration.

Yet a similar problem has been overcome by life on Earth. The single-celled algae known as phytoplankton, which are a major part of the plankton living on the surface of the seas, are heavier than water and will sooner or later sink permanently below a level at which photosynthesis is possible. Eddies in the water help to keep the phytoplankton at the surface and in enough light, and before they eventually sink and die they must reproduce. They have been remarkably successful at doing so. For much of life's history on Earth, phytoplankton must have been a major feature of the biosphere. So could life survive the convection currents within gas giants? Perhaps it could. Not necessarily in Jupiter or Saturn, but maybe in the gas giants of other planetary systems – or even in Uranus or Neptune, where convection currents are not so strong.

But the basic obstacle remains: the layers of atmosphere with the right substances for the origin of life may not coincide with the right temperature range. According to NASA's data, Jupiter may get far too hot too quickly, although the temperature gradient within Saturn is less steep.

Life in these strange worlds could be even more interesting than life on another terrestrial-type planet like Mars. But gas giants – here or in other planetary systems – would not be planets for technological ETIs. They could not evolve in one. It would be more unlikely than a technological species evolving in the sea here, where at least there is a sea-bed with a wide range of habitats and materials for potential technology.

What, one wonders, would become of life forced to continue to evolve in a primordial atmosphere? Would it remain in bacterial form as certain microbes which continue to live in oxygen-free habitats on Earth – in the primordial way? Or is it simply that the limited range of habitats on Earth still devoid of oxygen restricts their present-day inhabitants to the microsco-

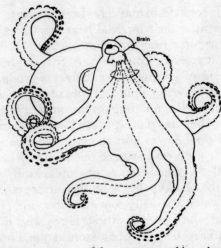

The central nervous system of the octopus and its relatives (the group known as 'cephalopods') has evolved independently from the vertebrates, yet laboratory experiments show that it functions in the same way. The cephalopods are the only group of animals to have evolved the same type of intelligence as the vertebrates. At one time in Earth history, the cephalopods must have competed with the fishes, the first real vertebrates, from which evolved all sizeable land animals. All animals with backbones (including ourselves) originated from certain lung fish. One cannot help wondering what might have happened had the fishes not existed, or had failed as a lifeform? Would the cephalopods have evolved into the first major land animals and gone on to dominate the Earth as the many groups of vertebrates have done? All we know is that they have not evolved into potential technologists in the sea.

---

pic? For all we know, evolution in a permanent primordial atmosphere, like that of a gas giant, might create a rich range of life, though it seems unlikely because the range of habitats would be very limited in a gas giant. Nevertheless, it may not be impossible that life, like planets, falls into two main categories: primary life in primary life-zones, and secondary life like ours, which lives in a planet's second atmosphere. Whatever the truth may be, the prospect of close investigations of the gas giants is fascinating for anyone interested in the possibility of extraterrestrial life.

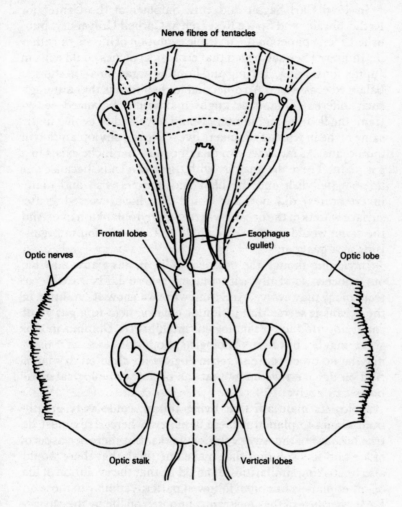

Nerve fibres of tentacles

Frontal lobes

Esophagus (gullet)

Optic nerves

Optic lobe

Optic stalk

Vertical lobes

The top view of the octopus brain shows a different structure from the brains of vertebrates. But experiments indicate that it works like the brain of a simple mammal. Note the strange arrangement for the animal's oesophagus (gullet) which passes right through the brain. (Imagine everything we eat passing through the middle of our brain on its way to our stomach!) The mass of the two optic lobes of the octopus equals that of the rest of its brain, indicating the animal's visual capacity. The fringes of the optic nerves connect to the retinas of the eyes.

In 1976 Carl Sagan and E.E. Salpeter of the Center for Radio-physics and Space Research at Cornell University, published a long paper on the possible evolution of life on, or rather in, Jupiter. They suggested that ecological niches could exist in Jupiter for sinking, floating and hunting organisms – in short, a balanced ecosystem. An objection to their idea is that although such different organisms might maintain a balanced ecosystem, the floaters and hunters would have had to evolve in the same niche in which the sinkers live – like the phytoplankton in our oceans. As far as we can imagine, no other niche exists in a gas giant. There the analogy with the ocean ends, because our floaters (jellyfish and the like) and hunters (fish and many invertebrates) did not, and could not, have evolved in the surface waters of the oceans where our phytoplankton live. And the same would presumably apply to the evolution of organisms in a gas giant.

Intriguing though the prospect of life in gas giants may be, our concern is really with planets where ETIs capable of technology may evolve. And from what we know of evolution in the oceans it seems that a similar environment in a gas giant could not produce technological intelligence. Dolphin intelligence maybe, but no technologists. So it does look as if there may be no other route to technological life than on dry land. And on dry land we know that the necessary biological attributes can evolve.

Biologists maintain that living things would vary greatly from planet to planet, if there is life elsewhere. This must be true because of the way evolution works. But there are aspects of life and its evolution that make one think that there would also be striking similarities. It could be that the evolution of life on other planets has often followed patterns similar to those on Earth, because of the constraints imposed on life by the physical evolution of continuously habitable planets. We are only just beginning to appreciate these constraints, but we cannot begin to know the truth until we find that radio message from Planet-X. So let us now turn to the groups of astronomers worldwide who are searching for signals from other worlds, and consider some of the different systems being used and the kinds of signals the astronomers hope to detect.

4

Searching for
Alien Intelligence

IN CHAPTER 2 we speculated on the possible height of ceilings in the universe: scientific, technological and biological. The height of these would probably affect our chances of discovering evidence of ETIs whose messages we could eventually understand. The lower the ceilings, the better our chances. Indeed, unless the ceilings are low, we may never be able to detect the presence of any ETI. Nevertheless, our hypothesis in this book is that ETI activity may be abundant and varied enough for evidence of it to be detectable; and our initial concern is the detection of this evidence which would confirm the universality of life and intelligence. For the present, any understanding of it – if we could understand it – is of secondary importance.

Since Project Ozma in 1960, when Professor Frank Drake carried out the first search for intelligent signals from space, astronomers have carried out about 50 searches which have lasted from a few hours to several years. A few searches are more or less continuous. Drake used the then new 85-feet radio telescope at the United States National Radio Observatory at Green Bank, West Virginia, to study two nearby stars, Tau Ceti and Epsilon Eridani. He observed them (on a band of frequencies centred on the universal hydrogen line at 1.4 GHz) for 200 hours during a period of three months, using only a single-channel receiver.

Astronomers have so far searched for more than 200,000 hours. But one hour's searching now is a great deal more than it was during Project Ozma. The continuous and rapid advances in electronics and computer technology have made the hours of observing, from program to program, far from equivalent. For example, the continuous SETI program (called META) at the Harvard–Smithsonian Observatory scans more than eight mil-

61

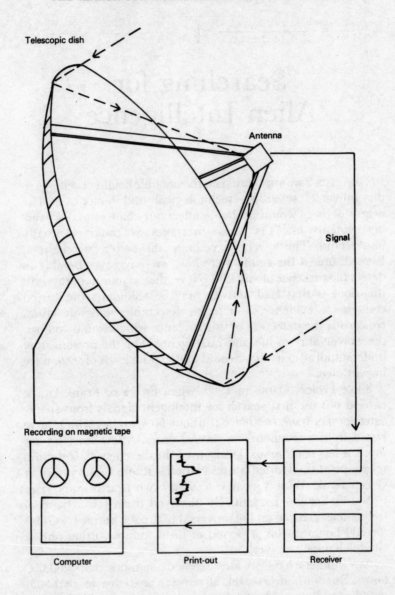

The basic components of a radio telescope. The dish receives radio waves from space and focuses them at the antenna. From here, the signal passes to the receiver. The received signal, which has been amplified several million times, can be seen as a continuous printout and recorded on magnetic tape or disc.

lion channels simultaneously. It can do more in a second than Drake was able to do in three months with his single-channel receiver.

Project Ozma 2 was also carried out at Green Bank by Dr Pat Palmer and Dr Benjamin Zuckerman during 1972–6, by which time several searches had been started in the Soviet Union, France, Australia and elsewhere in the USA. For 500 hours Palmer and Zuckerman searched the same part of the microwave spectrum as Drake had done (the hydrogen line at 1.4 GHz) for a sign of alien intelligence, their targets the possible worlds orbiting 674 Sun-like stars.

The SETI program at the Ohio State University Radio Observatory is the longest running continuous search. Dr Bob Dixon, who is Director of the Observatory, and colleagues started an all-sky search in 1973. This has continued 24 hours a day more or less uninterrupted, scanning a microwave band which includes the hydrogen line. During the years they have greatly improved their receiving system as new electronics and computer technology have become available. Besides the objective of discovering an intelligent extraterrestrial signal, Bob Dixon wants to proclaim SETI as a unifying activity for all nations, and he flies the Flag of Earth over the observatory.

Like other searchers, the Ohio team has had their share of false alarms, including the best known unexplained signal, the 'Wow' signal, so called because the telescope operator at the time wrote 'Wow' on the recording chart. The Ohio searchers, and others elsewhere, have tried to find that signal again – so far without success.

No messages then from other worlds; but Dixon did get a meaningful message from the owners of the observatory site who wanted to clear away the telescope to enlarge the neighbouring golf course, a larger golf course being more important to the business mind than the search for evidence of life beyond our planet. Dixon and his colleagues protested. Local residents also supported SETI in favour of golf. So did the local press. The story became of national interest. The plans for a bigger golf course were cancelled and the observatory saved, its site now secure for SETI into the foreseeable future, and a new kind of telescope for SETI is being designed. 'It will look in all directions at the same time', says Dixon, 'so eliminating the possibility that a transit signal might be missed by a single-beam radio telescope.'

WHAT KIND OF EVIDENCE?

Now the kind of evidence for which radio astronomers search depends upon what they think ETIs might be transmitting. The great difficulty here is that radio astronomy is a very young science and the transmitting ETI civilisations are, presumably, very old. Our best bet is to assume that we are about average; that many ETI species and their civilisations have evolved somewhat like ourselves, though probably on widely differing time-scales. We may be correct in this assumption, or hopelessly wrong. We may never know which, but we have to assume something to form any hypothesis that can be tested. At least that is *some* progress. Admittedly, the favoured frequencies already scanned carried no intelligent signal, but really the search has only just begun.

We accept that the evolution of technological species must produce curious, communicative, exploratory creatures. Therefore, we assume that for at least a period of their history some ETIs will be motivated in ways not too dissimilar from ourselves. We assume this much to guess what they may have done. If we think that all ETIs will be totally different from ourselves in their evolution, then we cannot guess their probable development and actions. It would be impossible and there would be little point in pursuing our subject. Yet we cannot but suppose that some ETIs will indeed be completely different from us, either because of their totally different biological histories or because they have advanced far beyond our present stage of development.

Evolution has generally made the mammals (the most intelligent animals) social, communicative and intelligent all at the same time. Together, these qualities have survival value. The evolutionary rule in higher mammals appears to be: an increase in the biological need to communicate for social purposes leads to the evolution of better brains and increased intelligence. We see the results of this evolutionary process in the whales and dolphins; in carnivores, such as lions and wolves which co-operate so effectively in hunting; and especially in monkeys, apes and man. And we can guess that the equivalent of a mammalian level of biological organisation is probably necessary for the evolution of enough intelligence to develop technology. Hence, ETIs are likely to be both highly social and communicative, as well as being highly intelligent.

I think we should note here that animals like our social insects, such as ants and termites, are not candidates for the evolution of technological intelligence. Their highly purposive patterns of behaviour are fixed in their genes. They are genetic automata. Every constructive action has been evolved. They could never build a radio telescope unless every stage in its construction was specified in their genes, which would need an unimaginably long period of evolution. It wouldn't be achieved, of course, since a radio telescope would hardly possess survival value for social insects.

Thus, we can confine our speculations to ETIs that are social creatures (although *not* like the social insects) with an innate drive to communicate – even if only in monologue, as we have with our messages on the Pioneer and Voyager spacecraft, which will journey undetected through interstellar space for millions of years. We can ignore the possible existence of ETIs which are totally different from ourselves and those which have advanced beyond our comprehension.

But without very low ceilings, to which the average technological civilisation could rise in several hundred years from our present level, there could be hundreds of extraterrestrial civilisations for every one that we could comprehend. And the gaps in comprehension could be hopelessly unbridgeable. An ETI which is no more beyond us than we are beyond our nearest relative the chimpanzee might not even be able to communicate with us across interstellar distances, even if it wanted to.

Let us imagine an even closer contact. Suppose some scholars of the Roman Empire, some 2,000 years ago, discover a modern library of science and technology which has conveniently slipped back into their time. These Roman scholars are as intelligent as anyone today, although possessing information and attitudes different from ourselves. But they possess a good deal of history and culture in common with ourselves. The gulf between them and the library is just 2,000 years of human history. Given that they could master our language, how long would it take them to understand modern science and apply its information? My guess would be at least several generations.

Contrast their problems with the problems – unknown to us – of similar people (ourselves) who may find an alien data bank, say on the Moon. We might be separated from the creators of the data bank not by 2,000 years, but by two million or even two billion years. And we are not only a different species, but of a different evolutionary biology. We may anticipate that our problems would be vastly greater than those of our Roman scholars. Only universal ceilings to knowledge and intelligence that are very low would make it possible for us ever to comprehend the contents of such a data bank.

COSMIC COMMUNICATION SYSTEMS

Some radio astronomers involved in SETI have defined an advanced technological civilisation as 'one having advanced radio techniques'. Admittedly, all advanced technological civilisations may have used radio techniques, but would they continue to use them? That is the question. Will our major means of communication of the twentieth century be the major communications technology of advanced civilisations in the universe? And that question also means: Is radio the ultimate medium for interstellar communication?

We know already that although a 'speed of light' system is highly satisfactory on Earth, it becomes less so for even relatively short distances within the Solar System. The unavoidable time-lag in communicating with the computers aboard distant unmanned spacecraft, such as those surveying the outer planets and moons, is already beginning to present problems.

A hundred years ago there were no radio communications on Earth. It was only in 1888 that the German physicist Heinrich Hertz discovered radio waves, and only in 1901 that Guglielmo Marconi transmitted the first message by radio waves across the Atlantic. So are we very bold – or very naïve – in thinking that civilisations that could have preceded us by millions of years will still be communicating by radio, although employing considerably more power to do so? Perhaps we are like the natives of Papua-New Guinea who used drums to send their messages, and who thought that more advanced people would communicate across the seas by using larger drums? Or are we like some of the North American Indians who, accustomed to sending smoke signals, thought that smoke rising to the skies from great fires would enable them to communicate with distant lands?

Those radio astronomers who search for ETI radio communications are assuming one of two things: either that no new physics which could lead to a more effective communications technology will be discovered; or that some ETIs will use radio frequencies (quite possibly an obsolete method to them) in order to find us.

It could be that no new physics will lead to a new and different communications technology, that we already have all the information the universe can offer for this purpose. In this case, we can count on virtually all communicating ETIs having reached the limit of technical perfectibility in radio.

But if radio is the universal ultimate in interstellar communications, there may be little two–way communication in the Galaxy, unless widespread colonisation has brought ETI civilisations within a few light-years of each other. Many ETIs could then be living in planetary systems to which they had migrated, in systems where no Earth-like planets ever existed or could have evolved.

The 'speed of light' limitation of electromagnetic radiation would even then be a severe frustration, but a 'waiting time' of a decade or two might be tolerable. We could then try to communicate with someone. Alternatively, if thousands of light-years separate ETIs it is hard to imagine much dialogue. Monologue, yes – but little dialogue.

If transmitting civilisations are relatively close to each other across the Galaxy, they may have established a communication network despite the 'speed of light' limitation. Signallers of earlier times, who were successful because of the close proximity of transmitting ETIs, could have developed a network which would encourage communications to continue.

Yet, if the laws of nature allow a quicker way, we cannot expect any super civilisations to wait even a few years for replies to their celestial messages. Of course, if the 'speed of light' limitation can be overcome, it would not matter how far apart communicating ETIs are; a network could be formed.

Therefore, there do seem to be two broad alternatives, assuming that we're not the only intelligent inhabitants of the Galaxy.

One: there will be many networks in a colonised Galaxy using electromagnetic radiation; or perhaps one major network if a faster carrier exists.

Two: ETIs will be in an uncolonised galaxy stuck with the

'speed of light' limitation for communications, and too few and far between ever to have an interstellar dialogue.

However, a few advanced civilisations may still be beaming their messages across the Galaxy without any expectation of ever receiving a reply.

WHAT FREQUENCIES?

Assuming that ETI messages are being transmitted by radio or by other frequencies of the electromagnetic spectrum, the main problem is the virtually limitless number of possible frequencies in which communications may be sent. Nothing could offer a wider choice than the electromagnetic spectrum. Background noise from the universe is at a minimum between 1 and 60 GHz, so we might expect a signal within this microwave band which can be observed from space without interference. From beneath our atmosphere, however, this interference-free band is reduced to 1 GHz to 10 GHz. We must also look within this waveband for specific frequencies, such as the hydrogen and hydroxyl lines, that might attract attention, especially where

---

Microwave Windows from Earth and Space.

(a) At low microwave frequencies (*left*) radio noise from the Galaxy interferes with observations. It is caused by charged particles interacting with magnetic fields. At higher frequencies (*right*) there exists quantum noise which is a natural accompaniment of all electromagnetic radiation. The 'quiet zone' between these two extremes is most suitable for observations; but the atmosphere does radiate in all frequencies within the window, especially in water and oxygen frequencies, as shown here. The band of frequencies from the hydrogen line (H) to the frequency of the hydroxyl radical (OH) is known as the 'water hole' because H and OH signify water (H_2O) to us, and it may also do so for other water-based life in the Galaxy. There is also noise from the cosmic background radiation, which is thought to be the result of the 'big bang' birth of the universe.

(b) The microwave window from space is wider, but is still limited by synchrotron radiation from the Galaxy (*left*) and quantum noise (*right*). The background noise from the birth of the universe is ever present.

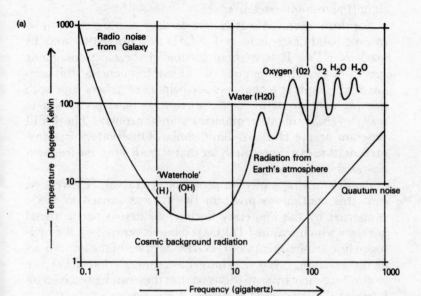

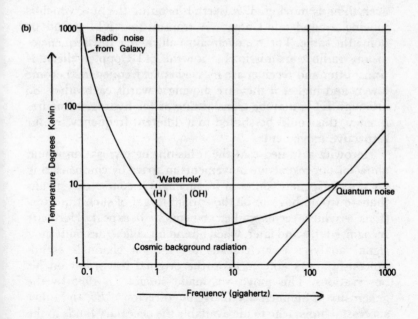

this coincides with the lowest energy requirements to transmit signals across interstellar space.

For this reason radio astronomers have considered the microwave band of frequencies 1–3 GHz as a range that may be used by ETIs. It is a small section of the electromagnetic spectrum though it contains two billion frequencies. But advances in computer technology are helping searchers cope with this problem. Systems (signal analysers) have been built to scan several million frequencies simultaneously. The SETI program at the Harvard–Smithsonian Observatory in Massachusetts uses a signal analyser that scans 8.4 million frequencies at the same time.

Paul Horowitz, a physics professor at Harvard University, runs this continuous program (which was started in 1983) supported by the Planetary Society. At first it had a signal analyser which scanned 131,000 channels centred on the hydrogen line at a frequency of 1.4 GHz. Because of the limitations of his receiving system, Horowitz assumed that ETIs are controlling their transmissions so that they can be received on Earth at the true (rest) frequency for hydrogen.

A problem for would-be interstellar communicators is that everything is moving. The Earth is orbiting the Sun, which is moving around our Galaxy. A transmitting ETI would be doing the same. These movements will change the frequencies of any radio transmissions – it's the old Doppler effect. If transmitter and receiver are moving apart frequencies become lower, and higher if they are moving towards each other. So although ETIs may be transmitting at the hydrogen-line frequency, this could be shifted to a different frequency by our respective movements.

Horowitz assumed that the transmitting civilisation would allow for our respective movements in space by compensating for the consequent shifts in frequency. Of course this means that we would have to be the special target of such transmissions – which seems rather too much to expect. Horowitz recognised this and later, when he and his colleagues built their signal analyser (which scans 8.4 million channels simultaneously), was able to drop the original constraint on his observations. This move was made possible in 1985 by the generosity of Stephen Speilberg, the director of *ET* and other successful films, who made available the necessary funds to the Planetary Society.

With 8.4 million channels being scanned the shifts in frequency produced by the respective movements of transmitter and receiver in the universe no longer posed a problem. Horowitz's continuous SETI program is now called META (Mega Channel Extraterrestrial Assay) after its advanced signal analyser which was put together at Harvard University. It has half-a-million soldered connections and the equivalent processing power of 120 mini-computers.

Horowitz and colleagues observe the entire northern sky in six months. The telescope, fixed into position while the Earth turns once on its axis, sweeps the sky one beam width of the telescope each day. A signal would be in the beam for about two-and-a-half minutes, and any interesting signals are stored for later examination. So far, they have swept the sky at 1.4 GHz (the hydrogen line) and at 1.7 GHz (the hydroxyl line).

SPECIAL RECEIVING SYSTEMS

The NASA SETI Program, the most ambitious endeavour so far, is a part of NASA's Planetary Biology Program which aims to understand the origin and evolution of life in the universe. Earlier searches have been able to investigate only a tiny fraction of our Galaxy and the billions of radio frequencies that exist, any of which might carry evidence of extraterrestrial intelligence. But NASA is taking SETI into a more comprehensive, co-ordinated and centrally controlled level of search. Some searchers believe that there is an even chance that by the end of this century SETI may have gained its first success, but of course no one really knows.

The Program was begun in October 1982 under the directorship of Dr Bernard Oliver, a SETI veteran. For several years scientists at NASA's Ames Research Center, the Jet Propulsion Laboratory and Stanford University, developed the receiving equipment, including computers and signal analysers, and a lot of specially written computer software – including signal recognition programs that enable the system to function most of the time without human attention.

Such advanced receiving systems make old radio telescopes and radar dishes adequate enough for SETI. The receiving and analysing end of SETI systems have been improved so much that they entirely supersede the equipment initially used by searchers. The NASA Progam is using, on a part-time basis, several existing radio telescopes and some old radar installations, including NASA's deep space stations. A few major radio telescopes, such as the 1,000-metre Arecibo dish and the 100-metre dish at Bonn, West Germany, are also participating.

The main task is the processing of the signals being received. After five years of preparation, Dr Jill Tarter, who has been involved in more SETI observations than any other astronomer, commented that 'Almost all our effort is devoted to the signal processing problem.'

A team at Stanford University is building a special signal analyser for the NASA program which will scan eight million frequencies simultaneously. Several copies of the prototype will travel from telescope to telescope with the SETI astronomers.

Like other SETI observations, the NASA search will run as automatically as possible. The programs and computer run the system, scanning the incoming radiation for evidence of alien intelligence, discarding natural radiation and human radio interference as far as this can be identified. The astronomers are only alerted when a possible ETI signal is picked up.

After some five years preparing the equipment and developing search strategies, the actual observations will take ten years or more. The observational part of the program will be in two parts: an all-sky search of five to seven years duration, and a target search lasting from three to five years. The all-sky search, as its name implies, will observe in all directions – at frequencies from 1 to 10 GHz. In the target search, astronomers will look at 1,000 selected stars and some unusual celestial objects, observing frequencies from 1 to 3 GHz, trying to find either a continuous or a pulsed intelligent signal.

With the 1,000-metre Arecibo dish, it would be possible to receive a signal from a similar dish 1,000 light-years away. In the all-sky search – assuming that the ETIs are using our level of radio technology – it would be possible to pick up signals from up to 40 light-years away. Nevertheless, most SETI scientists hope that ETIs will have more powerful transmitters than our radio technology can offer at present.

THE WATER HOLE

Decisions about which part of the whole electromagnetic spectrum to search remains a major problem. One interesting part

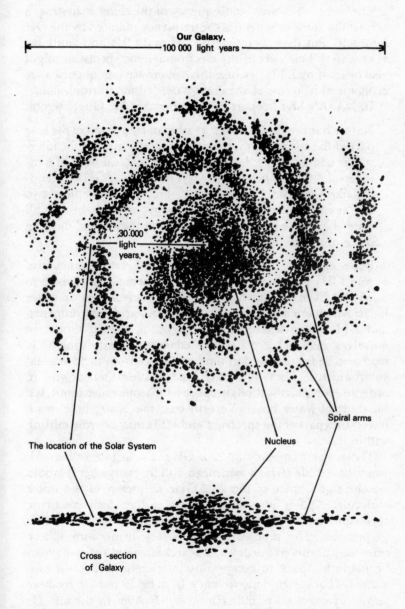

Our Galaxy.
← ———— 100 000 light years ———— →

30.000 light years

The location of the Solar System

Nucleus

Spiral arms

Cross -section
of Galaxy

When we see our place in a galaxy of 100,000 million stars – the Milky Way – we appreciate better the problems of SETI.

of the microwave band has been called the 'water hole' because at one end is the universal frequency of the element hydrogen (H) whilst at the other end is the frequency radiated by the OH molecule. Put these two together (H and OH) and you have H_2O–water! This part of the electromagnetic spectrum might also be used by ETIs because these microwave frequencies are economical in terms of the energy needed for transmission.

In NASA's SETI report SP-419, Bernard W. Oliver wrote:

> Nature has provided us with a rather narrow band in the best part of the spectrum that seems especially marked for inter-stellar contact . . . it lies between the spectral lines of hydrogen (1.4 GHz) and the hydroxyl radical (1.7 GHz). Standing like Om and Um on either side of a gate, these two emissions of the disassociation product of water beckon all water-based life to search for its kind at the age-old meeting place of all species: the water hole.

But would an ETI see the gap between these frequencies (of H and OH) as a 'water hole'? Are we being chauvinistic to think so? Even on Earth most animals never meet at water holes, which are a feature of arid and semi-arid environments, and ETIs living where water is plentiful, even if similar to ourselves, may lack a 'water hole' concept. Transmitting ETIs may also be far removed in time and space from their original environments. They may have long ago left their origins in order to evolve civilisations in space which, one must admit, is a bit short of water holes. Nevertheless, the 'water hole' is an interesting part of the spectrum and ETIs may be transmitting within it.

The water frequency at 22.2 GHz is also interesting. All water-based life (which *may* mean all life, everywhere) would see the significance of the 22.2 GHz frequency of the water molecule. And it is a specific part of the electromagnetic spectrum, unlike the 'water hole' which covers 300 million frequencies. The problem is that water in our atmosphere transmits at this frequency and searches would really have to be made in space to escape this interference. (See the two graphs of background interference, from below our atmosphere and from space on p. 69.) However, Dr Alan Bridle and Dr Paul Feldman at the Algonquin Radio Observatory in Canada did search the water line at 22.2 GHz from 1974 to 1976 when they observed 70 Sun-like stars within 45 light-years of the Earth.

Some radio astronomers and physicists have been studying the spectacular sources of the water frequency in the Galaxy. These consist of vast clouds of water and other matter which surround newly forming stars, especially the very bright O and B stars. Energy from these stars is absorbed by the water molecules and then pumped out at the 22.2 GHz frequency by what the physicists call a *maser* action (short for 'Microwave Amplification by Stimulated Emission of Radiation'.) A maser works like a laser, but the radiation is as microwaves instead of light, hence the 'M' instead of 'L'. About 300 of these vast water masers are known in the Galaxy, and the most spectacular radiates as much energy in the 22.2 GHz frequency as the Sun does in all frequencies. Radio astronomers have also discovered water masers associated with old giant stars at the end of their life cycle, so the water frequency is a prominent characteristic of the Galaxy. But presumably ETI signals would not be associated with very new or old giant stars.

RELYING ON CHANCE

However, where to look in the electromagnetic spectrum remains an open question. We have to try to guess the frequency on the basis of the characteristics it possesses. But it isn't really necessary to enter this guessing game as Professor Stuart Bowyer and colleagues at the University of California, Berkeley, showed in 1977 when they first began to use their SERENDIP system. Bowyer's team made up this acronym from 'Search for Extraterrestrial Radio Transmissions from Nearby Developed Intelligent Populations', because SERENDIPITY (the capacity to make desirable but unsought-for discoveries by chance) describes the nature of their observational method!

Bowyer and colleagues developed their system for several thousand dollars initially, plus lots of scientific labour and know-how. It's sufficiently compact to be transported from observatory to observatory; they can plug it into any radio telescope – where the astronomers are willing – without affecting the observations in progress. In other words, it piggybacks on telescopes being used for conventional radio astronomy, monitoring whatever is being received and rejecting everything except possible ETI signals. It's fully automatic and works 24 hours a day unattended.

On searching for an alien signal, Bowyer says: 'It's like turning on your radio and trying to find a station amidst all the static. We're looking for a strong narrow signal that could not be produced by anything in nature.' Extraterrestrial civilisations may transmit on a very narrow band of frequencies, or a single frequency, to conserve energy.

SERENDIP is an attempt to avoid the main problem associated with SETI: the shortage of time available on radio telescopes heavily engaged in astronomical research. And it also avoids the need to guess the best targets and frequencies to search – its search strategy is random. 'But it is searching somewhere, at some level of sensitivity, for extended periods of time,' says Bowyer.

The second version of SERENDIP is now in operation. It scans 65,536 channels and records unusual signals on disc, plus their frequency, power, time of detection and telescope direction. It ignores the naturally-occurring radiation which is being studied by the astronomers using the telescopes.

SERENDIP is checked out once each month, when some 4,000 recorded signals have to be explained. Most are from intelligent activities on this planet, or result from faults in the receiver, but the system is constantly being improved to cut down on the number of these false alarms.

FASTER THAN LIGHT

Now could it be that 'faster than light' communications (something based on *tachyons*) are possible and that ETIs are not using radio at all? Moreover, perhaps tachyons offer only one possible channel, or at most a few channels, so making the choice of channel in looking for ETI communities an obvious one. This is only speculation of course, but it's not impossible.

Tachyons, the theoretical particles that can travel faster than light, are at present the only means envisaged by physicists which might provide rapid interstellar communications. There is no limit to the speed of tachyons, except that they cannot travel slower than the speed of light. Although theoretical work on tachyons has been convincing enough to persuade a few physicists to set up apparatus and search for them – so far without success – most physicists think that tachyons do not exist. But no one can rule them out at present. The current theoretical framework of physics allows them to exist. Also, we have seen before that sub-atomic particles of theory have subsequently been discovered, even when their existence seemed very improbable – like that of the neutrino. However, unlike such sub-atomic particles (the existence of the neutrino was necessary to explain basic aspects of the physical world) the existence of tachyons is not necessary to explain anything. Yet if they do exist, they could completely change the significance of interstellar communications – that is, providing it is possible to build tachyon transmitters and receivers. I think that we can assume that ETIs would not be using microwaves or another section of the electromagnetic spectrum for their interstellar communications if a basis exists in nature for something far more effective.

Yet even if ETIs are both rare and have only radio for their communications, there could still be a few super civilisations with the energy resources to beam their messages across the Galaxy, or to other galaxies. Any reply we sent might take thousands of years to reach them, and two-way communication could not take place, at least for us. Great social stability and a remarkable constancy of attitude, measured by our standards, would be needed for a conversation lasting thousands of years. But societies may transmit information about themselves without expecting a reply, as we have with the spacecraft Pioneer 10 and 11 and Voyager 1 and 2. These will undoubtedly journey through outer space with virtually no chance of being seen again. In contrast, an automatic transmitter, repeating its message for a million years, might at least be detected.

It is also feasible that the individual members of some super civilisations live for thousands of years, long enough perhaps to have their messages acknowledged. There seems no obstacle to great longevity that we cannot envisage an advanced society overcoming; and electronic beings may survive indefinitely, for all we know. But for a short-lived species like ourselves, the existence of tachyons or their equivalent may be our only hope of an interstellar dialogue.

It can be argued, of course, that astronomers everywhere (in whatever ETI form and distributed throughout the universe in both time and space) will always be collecting information about stars and other galaxies, and other astronomical phenomena. Our present knowledge of the universe depends almost entirely upon one section or other of the electromagnetic spectrum, because all matter in the universe which is not at absolute zero radiates electromagnetic radiation from gamma rays to radio waves. Therefore, the technology that collects information about the universe by receiving electromagnetic radiation is unlikely to be a temporary technology.

Even if a more rapid carrier of information exists for communicating across interstellar distances, some ETIs may still send 'call signals' in one section or another of the electromagnetic spectrum because they will know that astronomers somewhere will be receiving it. And so some ETIs may choose frequencies of astronomical significance – frequencies that they know astronomers will be studying. But perhaps only 'call signals' are sent in this way. Tachyon technology, or some equivalent, might carry the bulk of interstellar communications, though the indications are that there can be no tachyon technology.

It may be significant here (in speculating about a new level of communications technology) that although the research effort in fundamental physics has increased enormously since 1945, it has discovered little applicable knowledge compared with pre-war physics. Of course it takes time for practical applications to be made of new knowledge, but even allowing for this, it is beginning to look as if the major technological advances based on physics – as presumably a new level of communications technology must be – may already have been made. The recent history of physics, the most advanced of the sciences, may be one indication that there exists a relatively low ceiling to science – and that most of the applicable knowledge in this field has already been discovered.

BETTER RECEIVERS

Even so, given that electromagnetic radiation is the only possible carrier of interstellar communications, the radio technology used in current SETI projects is a long way from any conceivable plateau of perfectibility. The technology is improving so rapidly that improvements will undoubtedly continue to be made in the decades ahead. Because astronomers are putting telescopes of various kinds into space, and may eventually have special telescopes there for SETI, we should perhaps ask when the 'limit of technical perfectibility' may be reached in this technology. The question is necessary because we can surely expect that ETI signals would be transmitted for a level of reception already at the plateau of technical perfectibility in electromagnetic communications. And this plateau would probably include having receivers in space and not under an atmosphere.

The plans for Cyclops, shelved some years ago for lack of adequate support, specified 1,026 dishes steered in unison by computer, each dish 100 metres in diameter. Cyclops could have been tied to the rotation of the Earth, like other radio telescopes, but continuous reception from any ETI transmitter would need two receivers, one on either side of the Earth. Cyclops could have detected a 1,000 megawatt beacon, one transmitting in all directions (omni-directional) at a distance of 500 light-years.

Perhaps it was best that Cyclops was shelved for economic reasons for a few decades. That way, a comparable receiver may one day be built somewhere in space where it could be permanently shielded from our radio and microwave interference. An alternative site would be the far side of the Moon, which is free from our radio interference. Such a project will probably have to wait until the first space colonies are established, although far more modest receivers will soon be put into space from where the detection of extraterrestrial civilisations could have an increased chance of success.

SIGNALLING BY LASERS

Soon after lasers were developed, it was suggested that the ultra-narrow beams of pure light (which lasers produce) might be a way of communicating across interstellar distances. The first search for extraterrestrial lasers was made from the Copernicus Satellite in 1974, when three nearby stars were scanned for ultraviolet laser lines. Also in 1974 Dr Shvartsman and colleagues in the Soviet Union began to use the 6-metre optical telescope at Zelenchuskaya, the world's largest, to search for very short laser pulses.

The idea that ETIs may have been trying to contact us with powerful laser signals has been criticised by some scientists who point out that laser beams, unlike radio beams, are visible. We might therefore have expected our ancestors in historical times (who were a good deal more aware of the night sky than we are) to have noticed beams of light in the sky. Yet there are apparently no records of any such observations.

But whatever section of the electromagnetic spectrum is used for interstellar communications – if it is used – it may not necessarily penetrate a planetary atmosphere. Since we have proved capable of being in space barely 200 years after the start of the Industrial Revolution, then virtually all technological ETIs could be in space. Another few hundred years and the Solar System may be thoroughly explored, with the number of space colonies increasing at an exponential rate. By that stage, there would then be many advanced astronomical facilities in space capable of receiving ETI transmissions. Knowing this as a probable development for technological species, transmitting civilisations may disregard the blanketing effect of a planetary atmosphere on sections of the electromagnetic spectrum.

I remember a well-known physicist discussing the problem of the atmosphere some 30 years ago and maintaining that advanced ETIs would make an allowance for receivers being restricted to planetary surfaces. This just shows how quickly our ideas change with our changing technological progress (though even today the thought persists in some quarters that the need to penetrate a planetary atmosphere would influence an ETI's choice of transmitting frequency). ETI signals may well penetrate our atmosphere but we cannot expect them to have been selected for that reason. Although the microwaves between the frequencies of 1 to 10 GHz do penetrate our atmosphere, this band is favoured in the search for ETI transmissions because it includes the universal hydrogen and hydroxyl lines and would make the most effective use of an ETI's energy resources. It is also little affected by interstellar dust and gas.

It could be that communicating ETIs transmit mainly to civilisations whose existence is known to them. Supposing that the first ETIs evolved on the first habitable planets of the Galaxy several billion years ago, the presently existing communications network may be somewhat more than well-

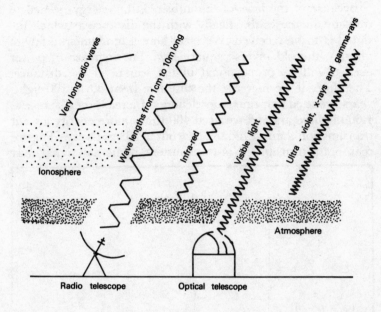

The atmosphere stops most wavelengths of electromagnetic radiation from reaching the surface of the Earth. And our knowledge of the universe still comes mainly from visible light and that range of radio waves which penetrate the atmosphere.

---

established and way beyond our capacity to detect or understand.

THE CALL SIGNAL

Perhaps our best chance is that a permanent provision may be made for new arrivals – for civilisations just emerging from their planetary egg. If so, a continuously transmitted 'call signal' seems the most probable evidence that we may find.

What form could the 'call signal' system take? Hopefully, it would be made as easy as possible to detect. It's been suggested that it might contain the minimum of information to allow the receiver to plug into a more elaborate transmission. If the call signal is sent by very advanced ETIs, it may be transmitted to reach most stars in the Galaxy, so that we might expect the transmitter to be in space and not directed at target stars.

Because of the laws of the universe, the energy needed to transmit increases drastically with the distance at which the signal is to be received. We meet here a fundamental law of physics: the old inverse square law. The increase in power needed will be proportional to the square of the distance. Therefore, if we increase the distance from 50 to 100 light-years, we need four times more energy. Increase the distance to 1,000 light-years and we need 400 times more energy for our transmission than we did to reach out to 50 light-years. For this reason, the transmitter (or transmitters) of the 'call signal' may

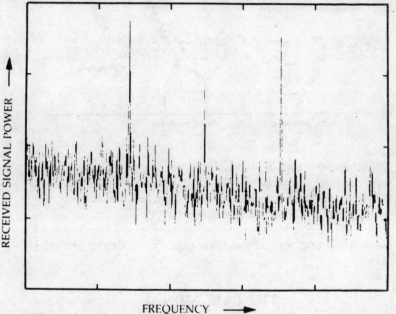

This oscillogram shows what an intelligent signal from another world might look like. But this one came from Pioneer 10 when beyond the orbit of Neptune. The three components of the signal stand out clearly above the always-present background noise. The signal from Planet-X might be this evident or very difficult to distinguish from the background noise of the universe and the radiation produced by television, radio, radar systems and other sources. But help comes from spectrum analysers that can automatically scan millions of channels per second, identifying possible intelligent signals from space for further study and observation.

1 An intelligent descendant of the dinosaurs – had they not become extinct 65 million years ago? Dr Dale A. Russell, of the Canadian National Museum of Natural Sciences, constructed this biologically credible creature to show what evolution might have produced. He based his creation on the characteristics of a dinosaur known as *Stenonychosaurus* (pronounced 'Sten-oh-nick-oh-saw-rus').

2 Dr Russell's reconstruction of *Stenonychosaurus* seen here with the intelligent dinosaur, was based on the fossilised remains of several specimens. The animal was about eight feet from head to tail and a meat-eater, judging from its teeth. What most impressed Russell was this reptile's relatively large cranium which indicated that *Stenonychosaurus* was probably as intelligent as a dull mammal.

3 *Homo erectus*, painted by Maurice Wilson, shows important activities which led to our technological civilisation, such as hunting and toolmaking – *Homo erectus* is believed to have been the first human species to use fire.

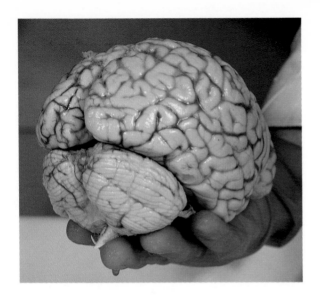

4   Human brains weigh 1000–2000 g, with an average of about 1,400 g. But a heavy brain is no certain indication of high intelligence as many talented people have had lightweight brains.

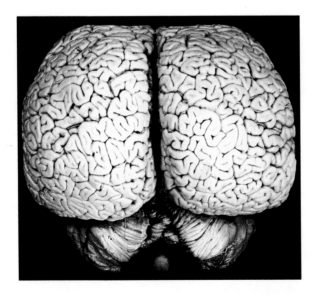

5   Brain of a bottle-nose dolphin weighing about 1700 g. With more convolutions than a human brain, it looks superior. It is a brain evolved for life in the sea, for hunting fish and seeing in poor visibility. Much of this super-looking brain has evolved to process the range of sounds used in the dolphin's underwater sonar system.

6   The plane of our Galaxy, the Milky Way, observed by the Infrared Astronomical Satellite (IRAS).

7   Section of our Galaxy looking towards the constellation of Cygnus. Many Sun-like stars here, but how many have planets like the Earth?

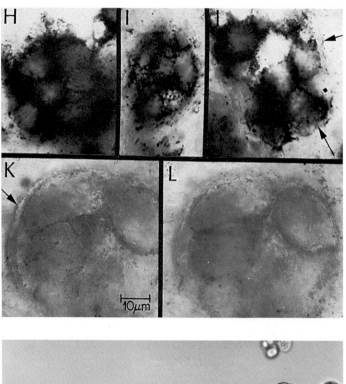

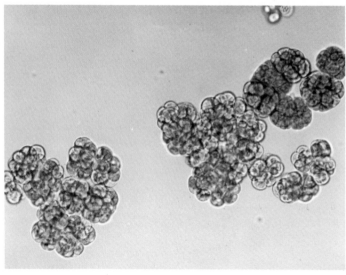

8 and 9   These fossilised bacteria from North-Western Australia are probably
the oldest known sheath-enclosed colonies of cells. They appear to have been
photosynthesising bacteria, like today's cyanobacteria (below). Professor
William Schopf, who provided this photograph, says: 'Together with other
relevant data, they establish that microbial communities were extant, mor-
phologically varied, and possibly physiologically advanced as early as 3.3 to 3.5
billion years ago.'

10   One of the oldest known fossils of a many-celled organism and one of many, dated at about 650 million years old, discovered by Dr John Cope and his students at a site near Carmarthen, South Wales. Most have the appearance of jellyfish, but there is also evidence of worm-like creatures. Only a few sites worldwide have such ancient animal fossils.

11   A primitive *calcichordate*, one of a large group of strange creatures which lived on the mud of shallow seas 600–400 million years ago. Some members of this group may have given rise to the ancestors of all background animals.

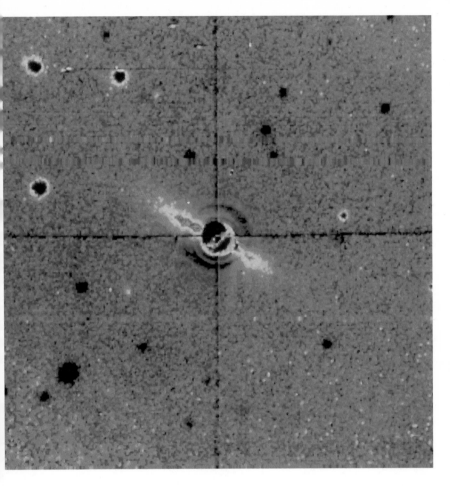

12   This most spectacular supporting evidence that planets form around other
stars was photographed by astronomers Rich Terrile and Brad Smith, after IRAS
detected intense infrared radiation coming from the star Beta Pictoris. The
amount of infrared from actual planets would be negligible (and not detectable)
compared with the infrared from the total surface area of dust and debris forming
this disc. It is thought that the embryonic Solar System may have looked like this
some five billion years ago.

13 In 1983 IRAS showed the bright star Vega had a cloud of matter in orbit. Here is an interpretation of that data. Vega is 50 times more luminous than the Sun and will burn itself out in half-a-billion years (one-tenth of the Sun's present age).

14 The constellation of Orion seen in the infrared – a very different view from that seen by optical telescopes. Assembled from the IRAS observations, this shows well-known regions of star formation.

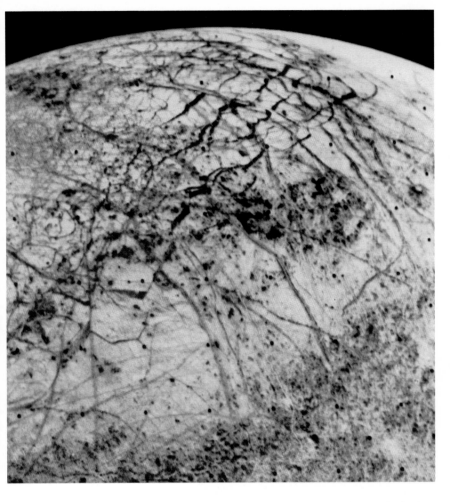

15 An ocean equal in volume to the oceans of Earth may exist beneath the icy crust of Europa, Jupiter's second major moon. Because Europa is being continuously distorted by the gravitational forces of Jupiter and its other moons, any ocean beneath the ice would be kept warm. Thus, it is just possible that primitive life of some kind may exist there.

16   Close-up of Jupiter's atmosphere, probably a cauldron of chemistry for over four billion years. Scientists have wondered if life could have evolved within this dense atmosphere. The ingredients and energy are present, but this environment may be too hot and turbulent for any form of life.

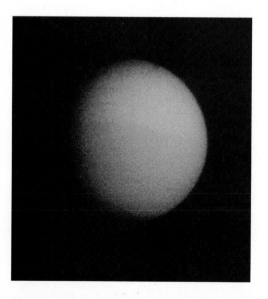

17 Saturn's largest moon Titan may be completely covered by a sea of methane and ethane. Its hazy orange atmosphere of methane ice, nitrogen and organic molecules is 1.5 times as dense as the Earth's. Thus, Titan is a possible site for some form of life, but only if a solvent other than water could be used in living processes.

18   Today only thin clouds of water-ice float in the canyons of Mars, but many photographs indicate that vast quantities of water once flowed on the planet's landscape.

19   NASA's proposed Rover vehicle, a version of which may be landed on Mars to search for evidence of past or present life and to study the Martian environment. Use of mobile robots will enable rocks from a wide area to be studied before selected samples are returned to Earth.

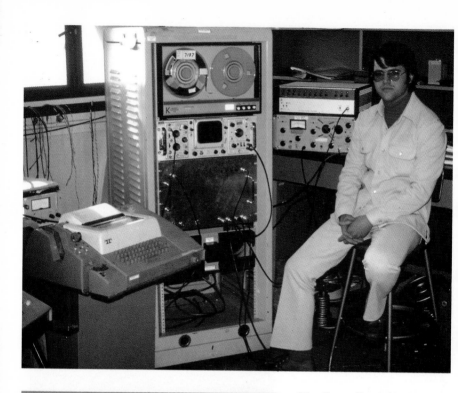

20   Serendip 1 in the rack next to David Langley who worked on the project with Professor Stuart Bowyer. The Serendip system can be used with any radio telescope without interfering with the observations in progress. Serendip receives all signals, but is programmed to reject everything except what may be relevant to SETI.

21   The Nancay radio telescope in France which has been used for a series of SETI observations.

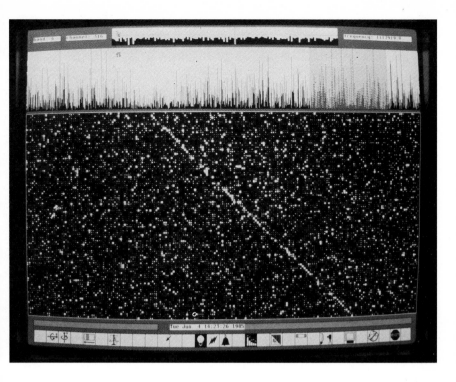

22   A one-watt signal from beyond the boundary of the Solar System was detected
during a trial run of NASA's SETI Program. It came from the Pioneer 10
spacecraft. Each horizontal line on the screen (there are about 100 lines) is divided
into 200 separate channels. Together these cover the frequency range displayed
across the screen. The 'snow' on a line shows the power (at one instant in time) in
each of the 200 channels. The Pioneer 10 signal shows up clearly and is slanted on
the screen because the Earth's rotation produces a frequency shift.

23   This signal from Voyager 2 was
detected when NASA's SETI equipment produced a radio map of the
sky in the vicinity of the spacecraft.
In this case the 'all-sky' SETI mode
was being tested. With the Pioneer
signal (above) the 'targeted' mode
was in use, i.e. the narrow-band
mode used to scan individual Sun-
like stars for intelligent signals.

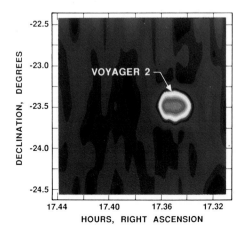

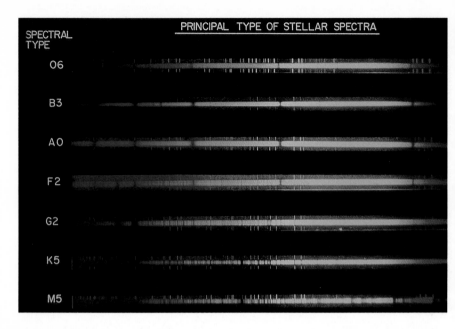

SPECTRAL
TYPE

O6

B3

A O

F2

G2

K5

M5

24   The spectra of stars show which are like the Sun and the best candidates for individual attention in SETI observation.

25   Radio telescopes at Goldstone, California, which are being used in the NASA SETI Program. These dishes are part of NASA's Deep Space Network for satellite tracking.

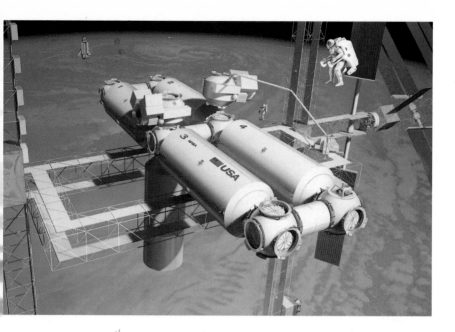

26   Space stations like this one, the McDonnel Douglas 6–8 man design for NASA, will lead to larger versions as the space age develops and their usefulness becomes indispensable to our civilisation. The next step will be the establishment of permanent space colonies.

26a   Artist's conception of the interior of a Bernal Sphere space colony.

27   Our blue planet photographed by the Apollo 17 astronauts on their way to
the Moon. Are such planets rare ornaments in the Galaxy, or the frequent
companions of Sun-like stars? Progress towards finding an answer is giving us a
new perspective. 'What was most significant about the first lunar voyage', said
Norman Cousins, 'was not that men set foot on the moon, but that they set eye on
the Earth.'

sweep the Galaxy with a narrow beam; the narrower the beam the less energy needed to sweep any given volume of space. We would detect such a signal as regular pulses of radiation. The length of time that we could receive the 'call signal', as it swept around the Galaxy, would depend on the relative positions of the transmitter and ourselves. Obviously, the greater the distance between us, the greater the spread of the beam and the longer we would be in it.

So where do we look for 'call signals'? Professor Joshua Lederberg of Stanford University has suggested searching the centre of the Galaxy.

The galactic centre is a logical site, but appears a rather precarious one for a permanent transmitter. According to current astronomy, the nuclei of galaxies are violently explosive. Explosions on a gigantic scale are photographed and studied, and there is evidence in the form of a rapid outward movement of gas in the inner regions of our own Galaxy that a similar explosion, one equivalent to the energy released by a million suns, took place there in astronomically recent times. Astronomers are not sure what exists at the centre of our Galaxy to cause such an outburst, but it could be a super-dense starlike object or a black hole.

In the days before radio astronomy, the centre of the Galaxy could not be observed. Vast clouds opaque to light hid the central regions from us, but these clouds are not opaque to radio waves and other sections of the electromagnetic spectrum. Radio astronomers have therefore been able to study the centre of the Galaxy in some detail. And they know it must be relatively small, because clouds of gas can be detected moving around it. Observations in the mid-1970s by astronomers at the National Radio Astronomy Observatory in the United States showed that the core of the Galaxy is no larger than the Solar System and is the most powerful source of radio energy known per unit volume. Astronomers have also detected bursts of X-rays from the centre, but nothing which could possibly be interpreted as an intelligent signal.

Yet astronomers have searched the galactic centre for intelligent signals. Because the actual centre is so violently active – and perhaps no place for a permanent transmitter – Dr Steve Lord and colleagues at the University of Massachusetts decided to scan the northern axis of the Galaxy. They tuned their receiver to the 115-GHz line of carbon monoxide, an abundant molecule in space which Frank Drake had suggested was the most efficient line (outside the interference-free microwave band) for space-based interstellar communications.

A different approach was adopted by Dr Jill Tarter and colleagues, using the Westerbork Radio Synthesis Telescope in the Netherlands. They searched for a pulsed signal which, they reasoned, would show up against the background of intense radiation in all frequencies emanating from the galactic centre. They envisaged the possible existence of something like a rotating lighthouse, with a very narrow pulsed beam of microwaves, which would sweep the Galaxy.

INTERSTELLAR EAVESDROPPING

Of course, we must allow for the great antiquity of any communications network which may exist within the Galaxy. Apart from call signals and messages transmitted by ETIs a little in advance of ourselves but still isolated, the main transmissions are not likely to be for us who have been in the electromagnetic communications business for less than a century. So what about the possibility of our doing some eavesdropping?

Our own radio and television broadcasts have already travelled 50 light-years into space. Powerful defence radar systems are also contributing to this expanding sphere of radiation. Such leakage from communications and radar systems may be less detectable than a signal specifically transmitted for detection, but it shows that eavesdropping on the communications of other worlds deserves consideration.

Dr Woodruff Sullivan and Dr Stephen Knowles have been the main investigators into the possibility of such eavesdropping. At a SETI symposium in 1984 at Boston University, they described their research. At first they decided to discover what any interested ETI might be able to detect if it eavesdropped in our direction, and they observed our television broadcasts reflected from the Moon, using the largest radio telescope in the world, the 1,000-metre dish at Arecibo. This provided the equivalent of a radio picture of Earth from deep space. One surprise was that the most powerful signal reflected from the

Moon turned out to be the United States Navy's space surveillance radar of which Sullivan and Knowles were completely unaware. 'The Moon, like the Earth, is remarkably bright in radio wavelengths,' said Sullivan and Knowles. 'It is a mirror of our technical civilization.'

Sullivan and Knowles calculated, from their observations, that the strongest of our television broadcasts could be detected up to 30 light-years away by an Arecibo-like dish. With NASA's Cyclops system (now shelved) an ETI could eavesdrop on Earth from up to 500 light-years away – of course, our television transmissions won't reach that distance for another 450 years.

It could be that our television and radars will be the cause of the first ETI signal being transmitted in our direction. There are about 100 stars close enough for our broadcasts to have been detected already. Thus, as our sphere of radiation from communications and radar expands into space the probability increases that we might just receive a strong and unmistakable ETI signal in reply.

It has been said that the leakage of television broadcasts into space may be only temporary, that within a few decades our transmitting systems will be more efficient and overcome this loss. Maybe cables of fibre optics will relay all transmissions. And if peace ever comes to Earth, our powerful defence radars would become redundant. But Sullivan and Knowles point out that other technological projects which leak radiation into space will follow television and radar. Large solar satellites, for example, may one day provide most of our energy requirements directly from the Sun. They would transmit the Sun's energy to Earth in powerful beams of microwaves and probably leak radiation into space in the process. Knowles has said that the minimum leakage of radiation to be expected from such a technology might be detectable 100 times further away than our present television and radar.

Another source of future radiation leakage might be powerful beacons for navigation within the Solar System. We can expect the Solar System to become rather crowded in the future, with a lot of routine transport requiring navigational assistance.

SIGNS OF ALIEN TECHNOLOGY

It might also be possible to detect nuclear fusion technology in space. An original search in 1983 by Dr Francisco Valdes and Dr Robert Freitas at the Hat Creek Radio Observatory in California attempted to do so. They were looking for the hyperfine line of radioactive tritium (H_3 an isotope of hydrogen) a by-product of nuclear fusion technology. Atoms of tritium radiate microwaves at 1516 MHz to produce this line, which is conveniently placed within the microwave band and therefore could be easily observed. If advanced ETIs are into the nuclear fusion business in a big way – perhaps carrying out the task of energy generation in space – then there may be enough of this by-product in the vicinity of their star (sun) to be detectable. The detection of a strong signal on this line would be very significant because there exists no known natural source of tritium in space and it has a half-life of only 12.6 years. Its production would therefore have to be continuous for it to exist at all.

In this type of search it is anticipated that ETI civilisations may reveal themselves by their advanced technology. And in the search for transmitted signals, it is assumed that ETIs will be sufficiently advanced and socially stable to broadcast across the Galaxy continuously – perhaps for many thousands of years.

MOTIVES: THEIRS AND OURS

These essential assumptions of the ETI's social and technological superiority leads us to realise that *their* motives for signalling to new civilisations and our motives for searching for their signal may be different. They will already know the score. We want to escape from our ignorance and isolation. Contacting new civilisations may be routine for them. There is nothing routine about our search. We want to know whether or not life and intelligence exist beyond the Earth, and our search for an intelligent signal is our only means at present of finding out. Later, we will certainly explore the Moon thoroughly and the rest of the Solar System where ETI visiting cards could possibly have been left during the past four billion years.

But for decades to come the only answer to our most fundamental question is in that signal which we may or may not find. For all we know, life on Earth may be a freak event in the universe. It may be an aberration of matter, rather than, as we prefer to think, an inevitable product of the innate processes of nature and an essential element in the history of the universe from its 'big bang' birth to we know not what. The evolution of complexity of matter from the simplest atom to the brain of human beings can be only a small part of that history. To discover something of our place in it is the driving motive behind SETI.

Some critics point out our unsuitability for a correspondence that may take thousands of years. And so it would appear for creatures whose lifespan is usually some way short of 100 years. Nevertheless, just the detection of an intelligent signal would justify all SETI projects. Those two persistent questions 'Is there life beyond the Earth?' and 'Are there intelligent beings elsewhere in the universe?' would both at last be answered 'At one fell swoop', as Shakespeare said.

Later a flow of information might start a new adventure for our civilisation, although nothing could equal in significance the first detection of that signal. It would be the most important discovery in history. For us the distance of the source would not matter much, except that its distance from us might indicate the abundance of transmitting ETIs in the Galaxy.

We would not expect to open a dialogue in the foreseeable future, and maybe it never would be possible. Perhaps only a few old and stable civilisations participate in the Galactic Network. They might be more able and ready to establish permanent transmitters in space; and the rarer the evolution of technological intelligence is, the more interested they may be in signalling their presence. For this reason, the argument against their being any ETI signals to detect, if the abundance of ETIs falls below a certain number, is really invalid. The motive for signalling will not evaporate if the evolution of ETIs is known to be very rare, providing that some ETIs survive to become very advanced.

Actually, the type of signal that might come from an ETI transmitter has already been discovered. One evening late in 1967 at the Royal Institution in London, Nobel laureate Melvin Calvin shocked us somewhat when he disclosed in a lecture on the origin of life that a radio source pulsating with incredible precision had just been discovered by radio astronomers at Cambridge. The signal, he said, was the kind we might expect to receive from intelligent life in other planetary systems. He said no more. Several days later, however, we learned that a new astronomical phenomenon – the pulsar – had been discovered.

The Cambridge astronomers themselves at first wondered if they had discovered an intelligent signal. Three weeks passed before they decided definitely that they had not. It was not long before similar objects, widely separated in the Galaxy, were being detected by other radio astronomers in other countries, as well as at Cambridge and Jodrell Bank. Each new issue of *Nature* reported a new pulsar, or so it seemed at the time. We were surrounded by pulsars, and a phenomenon repeated again and again had to be a natural one. Astronomers had in fact discovered the radiation from rapidly spinning neutron stars.

If the flashing ETI beacon is not found, many thousands of relatively nearby stars may have to be scanned individually for signals. But the chances of success this way are much reduced. According to the astronomers writing in NASA's 1977 SETI report, catalogues record only one in a thousand would-be target stars (F, G, and K stars) out to a distance of 1,000 light-years. This criticism was made because such target stars within this radius from Earth may eventually have to be scanned. They therefore recommended that a complete catalogue recording F, G and K stars out to 1,000 light-years be prepared.

However, research done after NASA's 1977 SETI report (see Chapter 3) has made everyone think again about target stars. It now seems probable that although stars with a long life cycle are necessary for the evolution of ETIs, the longest lived stars (K and M stars) cannot provide a continuously habitable zone for life-bearing planets. According to Michael Hart's work on computer simulations, target stars will be in the range F7 to K0. That is, between about 80 per cent and 120 per cent of the Sun's mass. It is therefore mainly G-type stars like the Sun which will be main target stars. Hart's conclusions are on the pessimistic side compared with other and earlier assessments of habitable planets for advanced life. Yet in an area where we must find our way so tentatively, we may do better by going for the pessimistic rather than the optimistic assessment.

Now let us look at the claims that extraterrestrial intelligence has already arrived here on Earth – in the form of ancient astronauts and present-day ufonauts (the reported occupants of flying saucers). We must examine these claims against a background of relevant scientific information, because if just one of those many accounts of extraterrestrial visitors happens to be true, we would have to come to a profound and rather discomforting conclusion. It would be that our Galaxy is colonised by technologically advanced beings and that they are right on our celestial doorstep.

5

Ancient Astronauts . . .
and All That

MANY ACCOUNTS OF visting extraterrestrials have been widely publicised in recent years. Their authors take themselves seriously. They believe in what they write. But I think that they seem oblivious to one item of information that drastically affects the probability of such visits: it is the age of our Galaxy. Those who search for evidence of ETIs in the records of history can cover, at most, only a few thousand years whilst any consideration of visits by astronauts from other worlds must cover the past few billion years. It is for that length of time – because of the age of the Galaxy – that ETI space technology has been a possibility. On statistical grounds Erich von Daniken's ancient astronauts, to take the best-known writer on historical astronauts, are not ancient enough – not by any means!

As the Galaxy is more than ten billion years old, our level of civilisation could have been reached a few billion years ago in planetary systems that formed a few billion years before the Solar System. This was possible as soon as stars like the Sun began to form. Therefore, the first technological beings to evolve have had so much time to develop their technologies that we can barely begin to imagine their achievements. But in their early days, say 1,000 years or so beyond where we are today, we can imagine their space colonies, probably similar to those planned by Professor Gerard K. O'Neill and others, crossing interstellar space, journeying from planetary system to planetary system, perhaps even before the Earth existed. And there could have been more to this interstellar travel than just a desire to explore the unknown. It is beginning to look as if factors inherent in the growth of technological civilisations may make space colonisation an essential development for survival.

The age of the Galaxy is an *essential* factor in considering the

possibility of ETI visits. The first civilisations to master interstellar travel may have had time enough to spread throughout
the Galaxy, not to the extent of occupying all planets (we know
this is not so), but they could have orbiting stations or colonies
in most planetary systems. Even late arrivals at the technological stage, say civilisations developing interstellar travel several million years ago, have had quite enough time for this.
Whilst we have no evidence that something like this has taken
place, it's not impossible.

As O'Neill has shown, a planetary surface is not the best
place for technological development which goes much beyond
our present level. It seems probable, therefore, that technological civilisations are soon forced to colonise their planetary
systems as a result of population pressures and shortages of
energy and resources. With the advanced space technology
which they develop, they may go on eventually to enter the
planetary systems of other stars where they may build space
habitats for themselves, mining bodies like the asteroids for
their purpose.

Already we can see how our own development, which may
not be dissimilar to that of other technological species, may
soon force us to build space colonies in order to satisfy our
increasing need for energy which we can get directly from the
Sun. The task of building solar satellites in space to tap this
energy may be performed by the first space colony – and this
colony would be the logical first step to major voyages to the
planets of the Solar System, and eventually to our neighbouring
stars. Thus, the Solar System could have supported ETI
visitors any time during the 4.6 billion years of Earth history.
When we consider the probability of visits in historical times
we must take this into account.

Now, whilst we cannot easily envisage beings of high intelligence leaving their advanced civilisations, to journey through
the cold emptiness of interstellar space for decades, in order to
colonise an alien planetary system, we *can* envisage it being
done using automated spacecraft. A small craft with artificial
intelligence (robots) in control might be launched to a neighbouring star to establish a suitable habitat, i.e. build a space
colony. The genes of the race that sent the spacecraft might
then be synthesised by the robots to start a first/new generation
of colonists. Judging by the way our fundamental biology and

computer science are advancing, such a task might not be impossible in a century or two even for us – though I can imagine a robot as mother-substitute providing a few biological and psychological problems for our species!

As the age of the Galaxy so affects our thinking about what the human situation could be in relation to life outside the Earth, we had better look at the ways in which its age has been calculated. This is very important. If the Galaxy was much younger, say not much older than the Sun, then we could entertain the thought that we are probably among the first wave of technological species to have evolved; there would be no apparent paradox in the absence of evidence of ETI visits. But in a Galaxy more than twice the age of the Sun, we cannot be amongst the first.

One does hear a lot about this paradox, which Fermi's question posed many years ago, but really it is only an apparent paradox. I think that those who emphasise it forget the old saying that 'absence of evidence is not the same as evidence of absence'. We could even speculate that large ETI space colonies are within the Solar System and the source of the UFO phenomenon. No one could state definitely that this is not so because if they were suitably stationed in orbit we could not detect them. For instance, it was only in 1979 that two new moons of Jupiter were discovered. The first, photographed by Voyager 1, is 70–80 kilometres across; the second, photographed by Voyager 2, is 30–40 kilometres across. Since then Voyager 2 has discovered *ten* previously unknown moons orbiting Uranus. Most are about 70 kilometres in diameter – but one is 170 kilometres across!

HISTORY OF THE GALAXY

Let us break here for a moment and consider the age and history of the Galaxy. We need to know how long stars like the Sun have been forming with its range and abundance of elements, especially heavy elements. Heavy elements (mainly metals) have been essential for the growth of our civilisation and the same must apply on other worlds. The incorporation of heavy elements into earlier planetary systems obviously depended on these elements having been synthesised in the early history of the Galaxy, probably by generations of very massive and short-lived stars.

All elements heavier than hydrogen and helium, the two lightest, have been synthesised within stars. Helium is thought to have existed since the 'big bang', but it is also continually formed by the stars. The main energy source in all stable stars comes from the 'burning' of hydrogen into helium (the nuclear fusion of the hydrogen bomb). Only stars provide enough heat to form elements heavier than helium. All elements heavier than iron (which at an atomic weight of 56 is 'halfway up' the atomic scale) can be formed only by stars several times as massive as the Sun when they end their life cycles in supernovae explosions.

Many astronomers think that the first massive stars may have carried out such synthesis relatively quickly. The Fraunhofer lines of heavy elements exist in the spectra of all stars. Fraunhofer lines show on the spectroscope like finger-prints; each element has its own distinct set because every element absorbs radiation and radiates it at its own specific wavelengths, thus producing lines which can be observed. Most astronomers think that the elements which can be observed in the stars have existed in their present relative abundance for the greater part of the Galaxy's history. According to modern theory, the Galaxy looked more or less as it does today after its initial few hundred million years of evolution.

Astronomers have found no stars without a proportion of heavy elements, although some have far less than the Sun. A star listed astronomically as HD 122563 has the smallest known proportion of heavy elements – reported to be 300 times less than in the Sun. Stars like HD 122563 are very rare and among the oldest in the Galaxy. Older stars, the first stars, no longer shine. Almost all must have consumed their nuclear fuel long ago, although they will still exist as celestial cinders – or as black holes.

The first stars could not have been like the stars that formed at a later stage. Only the original elements of the universe, hydrogen and helium, were available at their formation. They must have lacked completely all heavier elements. Such stars are the 'missing links' of stellar evolution, and any that still shine must be very small stars indeed. Being of small mass they would 'burn' slowly and have a long life cycle; but consequently they would be so dim that they might never be detected.

The important point for our subject is that most stars, many of which must be far older than the Sun, have an abundance of heavy elements. This suggests that any planets which they may possess will not differ much in composition from those of the Solar System. Obviously, rocky planets like Mercury, Mars, Venus and Earth could not form unless the protostar which gave them birth had sufficient heavy elements.

AGE OF THE GALAXY

Astronomers have used three independent ways to calculate the age of the Galaxy. Approximately, each way gives a similar age, which enables one to conclude that the Galaxy must be *at least* ten billion years old:

1   The radioactive dating of the Galaxy depends upon certain radioactive elements. The present ratios of uranium 235 to uranium 238, thorium 232 to uranium 238, lead 244 to uranium 238, and rhenium to osmium are measured. The ratios that now exist depend on when these elements were formed by the first generations of massive stars in the Galaxy. And since we know the atomic decay rates involved, we can work out (from the present ratios) when these elements were first formed in the Galaxy. Thus, the above elements give us four independent radioactive clocks from which an age for the Galaxy of from 10 to 20 billion years can be calculated. In 1982 Professor Hans Klapdor, at the Max-Planck Institute for Nuclear Physics, Heidelberg, and his collaborators, showed that an age nearer the 20-billion-year mark is more likely. Their research, which is regarded as an important contribution to the subject, made new calculations of what the ratios of the 'radioactive clock' elements would have been when first formed.

2   If we accept (as do most astronomers nowadays) that the universe has been expanding since the 'big bang' then the red-shifts in the spectra of galaxies and other extragalactic objects indicate the rate of expansion of the universe, and so provide a measure of its age. By going back in time, we can reach a point before which the density of matter was too great to have allowed galaxies to form.

The universal background radiation of three degrees Kelvin

(that is, three degrees above absolute zero), which Penzias and Wilson discovered in 1963, and for which discovery they received a Nobel Prize in 1978, is generally accepted as the energy from the initial fireball dissipated with the expansion of the universe from many millions of degrees to 3°K. Therefore, this provides additional support for the age of the universe (and the age of galaxies) from its expansion since the 'big bang'. Again an age of between ten and twenty billion years can be calculated.

3   The Galaxy must be older than its oldest stars and the ages of its oldest stars can be estimated. The oldest collection of stars exist in what are called globular clusters, of which there are over 100 situated mainly in the halo of the Galaxy. Each globular cluster consists of hundreds of thousands of stars. All the stars in each globular cluster must have formed at the same time in the same conditions and from the same cloud of matter, so that initially all stars in each cluster had roughly the same composition. There was just one variable: their original masses were different. And this accounts for their present observable differences. As gravity has permanently locked the stars of each globular cluster together, astronomers can compare the results of billions of years of stellar evolution because the rate at which stars within a cluster have evolved their present observable state has been determined solely by their original mass.

Differences in mass have very important consequences for stars. The greater the mass, the faster the rate at which a star 'burns' its substance. Indeed, the luminosity of a star, which results from its rate of 'burning' hydrogen into helium, varies as the cube of its mass for those stars which are more than three times as massive as the Sun. So, for example, a star ten times the mass of the Sun will 'burn up' its substance 1,000 times faster. Massive stars, therefore, pass rapidly through the stages of stellar evolution to end as supernovae, neutron stars or black holes, depending upon their original mass. Very massive stars, say 20 to 30 times the Sun's mass, can remain stable only for a few million years. Yet stars of low mass have long lifetimes. A star just 10 per cent less massive than the Sun will remain stable for about 15 billion years. A star 25 per cent less massive will last even longer, with a life expectancy twice that of the Sun.

No really massive stars now shine in the globular clusters which range in age from five to ten billion years. The stars that we see are the less massive stars which pass slowly through their evolutionary stages. That is, stars of about the mass of the Sun and less which have lifespans of ten billion years and more. The Sun in its senility – in about five billion years time – will become a white dwarf. It will then have reached the end of its active life cycle. Many white dwarfs which were once like the Sun exist in globular clusters.

VISITS TO EARTH

These three separate lines of enquiry lead us to think that the Galaxy has been more or less in its present condition for at least ten billion years, so that in theory ETIs could have visited the Earth at any time since its formation. A little arithmetic will show the implication of this for claims that we have been visited in historical times.

To make the arithmetic easy, we will let the Earth settle for a few hundred million years after its formation before we entertain visitors. Let us say that they could have come any time during the past four billion years, instead of 4.6 billion years, the accepted age of the Earth. And let us assume that the probability of visits remains constant during the four billion year period.

Now, most of the ancient astronauts popularised in newspapers and books are supposed to have come within the past 4,000 years of human history. Therefore, the probability of their coming just once in this period rather than at any other time in Earth history is 4,000 years into 4,000,000,000 years. This is the same as 1,000 into 1,000,000,000 which is the same as 1 into 1,000,000. In other words, to make just one visit statistically probable in historical times (in the past 4,000 years) requires that there were a million ETI visits to the Earth since its formation!

Even if we allow that the probability of a visit to Earth increases as the Galaxy gets older and more technological species evolve, the above sum would not be drastically altered. For ETIs to have visited the Earth in historical times, or in recent years as the occupants of flying saucers, our Galaxy would have to be teaming with interstellar travellers and thoroughly colonised. Otherwise, visits from those historical astronauts and occupants of flying saucers would be too great a coincidence to be credible.

ETIs who travel from their home planets to visit us, as science fiction writers have described again and again, are simply not probable. We should not expect such guests. That does not seem the way in which visits to other planetary systems may take place.

If interstellar travel and colonisation of planetary systems is widespread our presence may be well documented, especially as 'blue planets' like the Earth may be very rare. It has been suggested that for us to have been left undisturbed for so long we must be in a sort of planetary nature reserve. Presumably in such a situation there would be no motive for ETIs to leave visiting cards on Earth, or on the Moon. You don't leave signs in a National Park for the chimps to see that you've visited them. However, we could also speculate that our planetary system has been left undisturbed because if we go into space as part of the development of our civilisation we will need the material resources of the Moon and, more importantly, the asteroids. In a colonised Galaxy this need might be fully recognised and the resources of planetary systems with flourishing biospheres left intact.

Let us now assume that our Galaxy has not been thoroughly explored during the past few billion years and most of its planetary systems colonised, and that our presence is not recorded in a computer of the Cosmic Network. In short, that we are not in a planetary zoo surrounded by ETI activity of which we are unaware. In this case 'visiting cards' are worth consideration, since they could have been left at any time during the past few billion years.

It is hard to imagine a species like ourselves, with the motivation to develop high technology and to explore the universe, who would not leave a sign of its visit after crossing interstellar space to another planetary system, even if only to do no more than we have done many times on Earth: simply to mark the spot. But it seems improbable that they would do so as Daniken and several other writers have claimed, by putting their imprint on some ephemeral relic on Earth that would last at best a few thousand years.

Let's imagine that *they* (or their intelligent spacecraft if they

The message to star cluster $\overline{M13}$, our first message to the stars, sent by radio astronomers at Cornell University in 1974, using the Arecibo dish in Puerto Rico. This radio telescope (305 m in diameter) has a powerful transmitter which is normally used to bounce radar beams off neighbouring planets and the Earth's ionosphere.

Professor Frank Drake, then Director of the Arecibo Observatory, and members of the National Astronomy and Ionosphere Center of Cornell University, devised this coded message and tested it on colleagues to see how easy it was to decipher. It was then beamed at the globular cluster M13, some 24,000 light-years away and which contains 300,000 stars. At that distance the beam transmitted from Arecibo will just cover the 300,000 stars when it arrives at M13.

The message is in simple binary code, i.e. an 'on-off' signal. 'Ons' give you a 'one'; 'offs' give you a 'nought'. There are 1,679 components to the message. This specially chosen number can only be obtained by multiplying 73 by 23, so the aliens (who we assume are good at arithmetic) will see that they are able to construct a frame with 23 characters across and 73 characters down. All they have to do then is to interpret the message – which may not be easy for them.

(When this demonstration of interstellar broadcasting was reported in *Nature*, one of the world's top science journals, the message shown here was printed upside-down. Underneath was a cartoon of two radio astronomers receiving a reply. One was saying 'We've got an answer but they've reversed the charges.' Perhaps the high-powered editorial team at *Nature* should have underlined 'reversed' to make their joke more obvious.)

Reading the message (from the top right-hand corner) we have in binary arithmetic the numbers 1 to 10. This establishes the language of the message. The block of lines underneath gives the atomic numbers of hydrogen, carbon, nitrogen, oxygen and phosphorous, showing that all life on Earth is mainly composed of these elements. This information is then used to display the molecules that form DNA, and from line 32 to line 46 the double helix (our basic genetic mechanism) is shown.

The building-block representation of ourselves has its head between the bottom ends of the double helix, so that intelligent aliens in star cluster M13 should have no difficulty in guessing the chemical basis of our lifeform. The large vertical block between the two strands of the double helix provides the number four-thousand-million (4 billion) which is the estimated number of genetic components (base pairs) needed to code for a human being.

99

To the right of the human figure is the measure of our average height: 14 times the wavelength of the signal of 12.6 cm. To its left is a heavy block which also gives four-thousand-million, the assumed figure for the Earth's human population.

Under all this, reading from the right, we have the Sun and its nine planets. Note that the third planet, the Earth, is raised towards the feet of our symbolic figure. And beneath the Solar System is the Arecibo radio telescope. This is shown pointing downwards to a number which gives its diameter in terms of the wavelength of the transmitted signal.

This exercise by Professor Frank Drake and his colleagues nicely demonstrates the level of information that can be sent across interstellar space without much difficulty or expense – the whole message was transmitted in 169 seconds. And it gives some indication of what may be achieved by advanced civilisations who wish to communicate their cultures to other intelligent beings in the universe.

do not make long journeys themselves) came to the Solar System sometime in the past four billion years. That is, since life has been evolving and erosion has been a major force in shaping the Earth. What kind of site would they choose?

There is no reason to suppose that ETIs would expect a reply to their messages deposited on or nearby any world that they, or their intelligent spacecraft, may have visited. Radio astronomers in the United States have sent messages to distant stars with no expectation of contacting anyone. Their action was simply a tribute to the idea that intelligence lies 'out there'. The pictures and recordings in and on the Pioneer and Voyager spacecraft are similarly motivated. The purpose of the Pioneer and Voyager probes has been the exploration of the outer planets, and they and their messages will almost certainly never be seen again as they journey through interstellar space to eventual disintegration. Therefore, we can hardly credit ETIs with less generosity of spirit in their gestures towards propagating the fruits of their intelligence. Furthermore, if when visiting the Earth long ago, they foresaw the possible evolution of a technological species, they may have found some secure yet distinctive site at which to leave a message.

EVIDENCE ON THE MOON?

So where could a site be secure for millions of years? Not on Earth. Only on a body like the Moon, one free from erosion, could a sign last that long. David R. Scott, Commander of Apollo 15, said that he had great difficulty in coming to terms with the fact that a large rock in front of him on the Moon had been there virtually unchanged for more than 500 million years – before there was any land life on Earth. Alien astronauts landing on the Moon a billion years before Scott would have witnessed much the same scene, and it would not have escaped their notice that here was a good place to leave tokens of their visit to the Solar System. Anything suitably placed on the Moon, from a simple sign to an elaborate data bank, could have been left with the high probability that it would remain intact for a billion years or more. The Moon, one of the most inert worlds in the Solar System, is certainly a likely place for messages from ancient astronauts – if any have ever come our way.

101

There will be no signs of ancient astronauts on Earth: unless advanced ETIs surround us; unless they occupy the planetary systems of nearby stars; or unless they are established in the outer regions of the Solar System. The idea that ETIs would have helped the ancient Egyptians build the great pyramids – or the less ancient South Americans build their pyramids – as signs of visits to Earth is not realistic. Such signs would be too ephemeral by far, and subject to the interference of beings who would not understand the significance of an ETI message. But put the message on the Moon, away from such interference – and what is more important away from erosion – and there is the possibility of those ancient astronauts being understood by beings sufficiently advanced to cross space from one world to another.

Some years ago, in an article in *Spaceflight* (Dec. 1972) G.V. Foster made an interesting calculation of the number of possible ETI visits in the Earth's history. He assumed that one space-faring civilisation exists for every 10,000 stars. This gives ten million civilisations in the Galaxy. Foster then calculated that the rotation of the Galaxy would have brought more than four million stars within 50 light-years of the Earth, since its formation. He also assumed that his space-faring civilisations travelled up to this distance, which gives a total of 420 ETI visits to Earth. He went on to conclude that if this was so, the Solar System could be 'a well trampled place'.

It does seem now that this is not the most likely way in which the Earth has been visited. There appears to be no need for space-faring civilisations to cross any greater interstellar distance than that to the nearest star. (In our case just over four light-years.) Most stars may have debris in orbit suitable for building space habitats. And if interstellar travel is practical, there could have been far more than 420 visits to Earth since its formation.

BIOLOGICAL EVIDENCE

As we shall see later, there are possible biological consequences of visits in the past. We could hardly expect visits by alien astronauts without a few alien microbes accompanying them, unless they were well sterilised electronic astronauts. Two Japanese scientists, whose research is described in Chapter 9, believe it possible that ETIs may have tried to communicate with us biologically and that the evidence may still be around for us to discover. This doesn't seem very likely. It seems more probable that any alien organisms (say micro-organisms) arriving with ancient astronauts would either quickly die out or increase at the expense of Earthly forms, depending on their liking for conditions here. Admittedly, a large proportion of the Earth's living matter by weight is made up of micro-organisms. So there could be something alien hidden in the micro-world, although there is not the slightest hint of it; nor is there, one would imagine, any likelihood of discovering it even if there were.

Let us now sum up ancient astronauts. Only something approaching exponential growth of colonisation in the Galaxy could make possible ETI visits to the Solar System in the brief period of historical times, when those well-publicised ancient astronauts were supposed to be visiting Earth and helping mankind to develop civilisation. Otherwise, a vist here during that period, rather than to the millions of other planetary systems that we think exist in the Galaxy, would be extremely improbable. But given colonisation, ETI visits could be commonplace. That is why acceptable evidence of *just one* visit – either in historical times or today in flying saucers – would shatter our presumptions about the human situation. We would have to conclude that we are surrounded by alien intelligences and technologies superior to our own.

We will now look at why the colonisation of space may be an inevitable development for all really successful technological civilisations, and at how the new ideas about space colonies drastically affect our assessment of the chances of detecting evidence of intelligence beyond the Earth.

6

Could ETIs
Reach the Solar System?

THERE ARE TWO reasons why we must consider the possibility of travelling to the stars. Firstly, to see if we may eventually be able to do so. Secondly, and this is the main reason here, to see how probable it is that other civilisations may have visited the Solar System.

Numerous space technologists and physicists have written on the technical problems of interstellar spaceflight. Most grant its feasibility, although only in periods of time far longer than the present human lifespan. To reach the nearest star in a shorter time with a crew on board would take an unattainable amount of energy, even if the most efficient source theoretically possible were used. One day automatic probes may travel to the nearest stars, perhaps at speeds of up to a tenth that of light, reaching their targets within fifty to a few hundred years; but astronauts will not follow them in spacecraft as they did to the Moon. We must bear in mind that the nearest star is 100 million times further away than the Moon.

FOUR WAYS TO THE STARS

To travel faster than light, like Captain Kirk and his crew in *Star Trek*, we would have to overcome the barriers which the laws of the universe appear to have placed in the way. In theory there seem to be four ways to the stars:

1 By spacecraft that travel at almost the speed of light.

2 By much slower craft in which the travellers would survive in suspended animation of some kind (deep-frozen or in hibernation, perhaps) for most of the voyage.

3   By travelling in space colonies, self-contained worlds, at relatively slow speeds. In this way, only future generations would eventually colonise other worlds.

4   By using computers or robots to do the travelling for us. That is, advanced artificial intelligences. Add advanced biological techniques and the robots could synthesise the genes of their makers on arrival at a suitable destination. Or maybe the cells of the colonising species could be carried in suspended animation to other stars. And once the robots had built a suitable habitat in the new star system, the synthesised genes or the genetic materials of the living cells could be used to grow the first generation of a new civilisation. In this way, an advanced species could colonise other worlds without any individual of that species ever having to leave the 'home' planetary system and travel to the stars.

SPEED-OF-LIGHT FLIGHT?

Let's look first at what may prevent spacecraft ever travelling at speeds approaching that of light.

Einstein's Special Theory of Relativity, published in 1905 and confirmed over many years by a range of observations and experiments, forbids anything being accelerated past the speed of light. As matter is accelerated, its mass increases. Normally, this is undetectable, but the increase in mass rises sharply near the speed of light. Therefore, the amount of energy needed to accelerate anything (a spaceship or a sub-atomic particle) also rises sharply near the speed of light. Physicists can accelerate sub-atomic particles to 99.9 per cent of the speed of light, but they cannot accelerate particles to the speed of light. According to Einstein's theory, such particles – or a spaceship – would have infinite mass at the speed of light and therefore infinite energy would be needed to accelerate them further. Clearly, this is not possible.

ENERGY

Nevertheless, spaceflight at speeds just below that of light is not impossible in theory, however impossible it may seem in practice. And it does offer a fascinating advantage if ever it could be achieved. Not only does mass increase but time for the passengers drastically decreases as their craft nears the speed of light. But before we get carried away by this advantage, we had better examine an energy source that would give our spacecraft sufficient acceleration.

The most powerful energy source today is nuclear fusion, displayed by the Sun, the stars and hydrogen bombs. Hydrogen combines to form helium, but less than one per cent of the matter involved in the reaction is released as energy. A little matter converts into a lot of energy – as we know only too well from hydrogen bomb explosions – but not enough energy to transport us swiftly to the stars. Let's say that we would like to travel at 99 per cent the speed of light. Then if we used a nuclear fusion rocket to make a return trip to Proxima Centauri, 4.5 light-years away and the nearest star, the fuel would weigh one billion times as much as the spaceship. We can improve on this if we travel at only one tenth the speed of light and collect all the fuel for the return journey when we reach Proxima Centauri. The weight of fuel at departure could then be reduced to a few hundred times the weight of the spaceship, though the return trip would take 100 years or so.

But nuclear fusion is less than one per cent efficient – only 0.7 per cent of matter is converted into energy. What we need is the most efficient energy source theoretically possible. That is, the matter-antimatter reaction. Sub-atomic particles of matter and antimatter are frequently made to collide in giant accelerators during major experiments on the structure of matter. In this reaction *all* matter is transformed into energy. Yet even if antimatter could be produced in large quantities – and kept from contact with ordinary matter – it would not be a practical source of energy for near speed-of-light travel.

Let us imagine that a crewed spaceship, built in orbit, is propelled by the most efficient energy source we can envisage (matter-antimatter annihilation). It is accelerated to 99 per cent of the speed of light on a voyage to the nearest star, Proxima Centauri. This is done at a rate that will provide a force equal to the Earth's gravity (1g) for the passengers. Slightly higher and the acceleration would be uncomfortable; much higher and it would kill the passengers.

A spaceship accelerated to give a constant 1g would reach 99 per cent of the speed of light in six months. It would continue at that speed until six months before reaching its destination. It would then be decelerated to give lg. The same procedure would have to be repeated on the return journey. The energy needed for these four manoeuvres, even using a matter-antimatter reaction would need a mass ratio of 40,000:1. In other words, the mass of the fuel would be 40,000 times that of the spaceship. The complete spaceship at departure would be 40,000 times the mass of the spaceship on its return to Earth orbit. No one anywhere, I think, is likely to use such an impractical means of journeying to the stars.

And there is yet another obstacle to near 'speed of light' travel. It is the impact of atoms and interstellar dust, which would cause continuous explosions on the spaceship's shielding. Either heavy shielding would be needed, or energy would have to be used to create some kind of field with force sufficient to deflect interstellar particles – if such protection is possible. The nature of the universe is therefore against space travel at speeds anywhere near that of light. Sadly, the spaceships of *Star Trek* and *Star Wars* may remain forever fantasy.

WHAT KIND OF CREW?

Yet interstellar travel looks feasible enough at much slower speed. The ratio of energy to spaceship mass could be as low as 4:1, even by use of nuclear fusion as the energy source, providing that journeys of several centuries to the nearest stars were acceptable. But for travel times of several centuries duration (supposing human beings and not intelligent machines to be the travellers) space colonies would be needed in which generations live and die. Here the apparently insoluble physical problems of energy and mass would be replaced by biological and psychological problems which may also be insoluble. Could suitable people be found, who would be prepared to leave their home planet in the Solar System to drift off into limitless space, never to return?

FUTURE SOLUTIONS

We can see lines of research that may solve these problems. Rather than having generations living and dying on board space colonies bound for nearby stars, we may find ways of allowing those present at departure to be present when the colony arrives at its destination. While space technologists and physicists publish papers on interstellar flight, biologists study the phenomenon of ageing, with the prospect in mind of one day extending the human lifespan. Already the lifespans of small mammals such as mice and rats have been doubled by no more than restricted feeding from birth.

Some biologists are also working on the biochemistry and physiology of hibernation, on suspending normal animation by freezing and on ways of breeding animals artificially from conception to birth. One day, we will understand the biology and biochemistry involved and may be able to apply it to humans, if the need arises, thus perhaps easing our passage to the stars.

At the same time, people in computer technology are producing artificial intelligence and primitive mobile computers. Thus, one day a human level of intelligence may be simulated in computer form. Indeed, it may come before biologists can find ways of suspending animation or extending the human lifespan significantly. After all, the present rate of advance in the technology of artificial intelligence is greater than that of any other technology.

Given really intelligent computers, there is an attractive alternative to hibernating or deep-freezing interstellar travellers. The alternative would be 'terminal conception'. Only deep-frozen sperm and ova would be packed aboard the spaceship or colony, so that their DNA could be combined. The resulting human beings could then grow up and be educated in time for their arrival, or when a suitable habitat had been built for them. This process would be overseen by intelligent computers, all the way from embryo to touchdown training. It could be though, that it is not possible to keep sperm and ova alive for the duration of an interstellar journey. In which case, the artificial intelligences may have to synthesise the genes necessary to produce the first generation of a new civilisation. Anyway, that is the scenario, and it may be possible one day.

INTERSTELLAR TRAVEL BY ROBOTS

Once high artificial intelligence is achieved and given mobility, some of the science fiction writers' dreams could become reality. Our robot servants (or maybe our eventual masters, if things go wrong) will be ready for all tasks, including interstellar travel. The computers would depart, periodically reporting their findings to Earth. Hundreds or thousands of years later, they might even return with specimens to astonish everyone, just like the explorers of the fifteenth and sixteenth centuries returning with exotic gifts to astonish the royal courts of Europe.

Thus, if computer technologists and biologists achieve what we expect – and there seems no reason why they should not – then the main problems of interstellar travel and the exploration of the worlds of other stars could be overcome. The energy needed to approach the speed of light, which it seems impossible to provide, would not be needed. Virtually immortal computers of high intelligence could voyage through space for centuries, even millennia, in relatively small spacecraft which would need only a relatively moderate amount of fuel to send them on their way. Interstellar space may indeed be a formidable barrier – but not the ultimate and insurmountable barrier that keeps civilisations always within their own planetary systems. Although whirlwind tours of the Galaxy may remain forever fiction, there could be an abundance of interstellar traffic at speeds well below that of light, its technology as advanced as the laws of the universe allow.

There has been some discussion about the use of so-called von Neumann machines as interplanetary probes. In 1948 the great mathematician John von Neumann put forward a theory of self-reproducing machines or robots. He called them 'self-reproducing automata' and said that they would need four components:

1   an automated manufacturing facility;

2   a set of instructions or program (a computer program);

3   a means of executing the instructions;

4   a controlling mechanism to decide which of the instructions are carried out at any given time.

What von Neumann was describing (besides his self-reproducing automata) were the mechanisms upon which all forms of life depend, although von Neumann died some years before molecular biologists actually discovered the details of these mechanisms in living cells.

The von Neumann interplanetary probe would be a flying robot with a human level of intelligence. It would be able to reproduce itself after its arrival at a new stellar system where building materials in abundance would probably be orbiting the star. The daughter probe, or probes, identical to the initial probe, would then fly on to other stars where they, in turn, would reproduce probes to explore yet other stellar systems. Thus, the scenario is that in a very short time compared with, say, the age of the Earth, our whole Galaxy would be colonised by von Neumann machines. However, some think that such probes would never be built because they might become independent and evolve into machines with capabilities beyond the control of biological beings. A civilisation sufficiently advanced to make von Neumann machines would be a long-lived and stable society, probably with a high regard for its sense of responsibility. It would therefore not subject other civilisations to the danger of being taken over by intelligent machines.

Yet any extraterrestrial probe arriving here from across interstellar space, whether self-reproducing or not, would be perfectly designed for its purpose. We can assume that much.

PRINCIPLE OF TECHNICAL PERFECTIBILITY

There are certain principles which we may expect to be universal. One put forward some years ago by Arthur C. Clarke – the principle of technical perfectibility – states that technical inventions are taken to a level of development close to that which is physically possible. We can see this principle at work in past inventions, such as clocks, bicycles, steam engines and radio receivers. Therefore we can expect the same sort of development for our newest technologies, such as data processing (artificial intelligence) and space technology. Thus, if interstellar travel is possible, we may expect it to be developed to its level of technical perfectibility by civilisations more advanced than ourselves.

Advanced ETIs may therefore use this technology to gather interesting information, employing robots to do the necessary travelling and exploring, rather than doing it themselves.

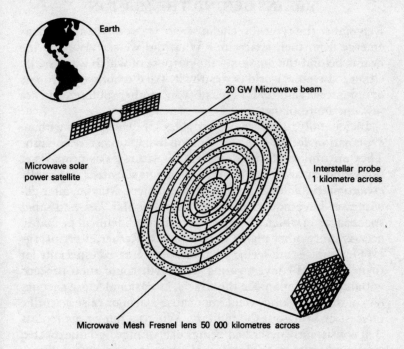

Earth

20 GW Microwave beam

Microwave solar
power satellite

Interstellar probe
1 kilometre across

Microwave Mesh Fresnel lens 50 000 kilometres across

An imaginative way to explore another planetary system, 'Starwisp'
is a unique design for an interstellar probe by Dr Robert Forward of
the Hughes Research Laboratory, in California. It would be just 1 km
across and weigh only 20g, so the energy required to send it at
one-fifth the speed of light to Alpha Centauri (which it would reach 21
years later) would be far less than that required to propel a small
conventional probe up to that speed.

'Starwisp' would be a wire mesh sail of microcircuits, accelerated
by a beam of microwaves. Twenty billion watts of energy would be
used. This would come from a solar satellite, seen here in Earth orbit,
which would be borrowed for one week to send 'Starwisp' on its way –
at one-fifth the speed of light. The energy would be focused on the
probe by a lightweight Fresnel lens 50,000 km across – which does
seem incredibly huge. The light-sensitive microcircuits of 'Starwisp'
would send photographs of the Alpha Centauri system, including
any planets, back to Earth. It would be a flypast mission, passing
right through the system and on into interstellar space.

111

BRAINS BEHIND THE MISSION

Remember the typical scene in science fiction when the aliens emerge from their spaceship? What did we see? We saw the brains behind the mission – the purpose of which was usually either to save the world or destroy it. We did not see the robots or organic servants of ETI masters on another routine survey of just one more planet.

Incidentally, this scenario provides UFO advocates with an explanation for the appearance of flying saucer occupants. They are almost always described by witnesses as primates of some kind, an aspect of ufology which puts scientists, especially evolutionary biologists, right off the subject. Maybe, after all, witnesses have not been brainwashed by *Star Trek* and other space sagas in which *Homo sapiens*, or almost identical primates, occupy every other planet in the Galaxy. Rather, perhaps, the UFO witnesses are seeing what has been created especially for them. Any ETI investigating the Earth could then proceed without causing panic in the streets. Occasional 'close encounters of the third kind' would not cause alarm or raise scientific interest or bring out the military. Whereas numerous reports that consistently described beings of a strange and unexpected kind might attract the interest of scientists – and the military. But reports of beings differing only in superficial ways from ourselves, leaves scientists thinking that witnesses just lack the knowledge and imagination to make their illusions or hoaxes really interesting.

Let's move on now to what is perhaps the development that has most affected our thinking about the possible abundance or otherwise of extraterrestrial civilisations. Let's call it the 'colonisation factor' because it's probably the most important of the factors which are considered in any attempt to estimate the abundance, or otherwise, of civilisations in the Galaxy.

7

The Colonisation Factor

THE SOVIET VISIONARY of the space age Konstantin Tsiolkovskii, an ardent advocate for the hypothesis of the plurality of
inhabited worlds, wrote: 'Is it possible that Europe is inhabited
and other parts of the world are not'? It was a rhetorical
question put to evoke a definite 'no' in his readers. But on
reflection a qualified 'yes' is also a valid answer: Yes, it would
have been possible for other parts of the world to be uninhabited had there been barriers that we have not been able to
cross. Indeed many parts of the world were without human
habitation until recent times, when it became possible to cross
former barriers. Though humans (both *Homo erectus* and *Homo
sapiens*) had lived in Asia for thousands of years (more than a
million years in the case of *Homo erectus*) none crossed the sea to
neighbouring Australia until about 50,000 years ago, when the
first aborigines entered the continent. Even in historical times –
between about 1000 BC and AD 1000 – the Polynesians crossed
the Pacific Ocean in their big canoes to populate for the first
time the islands of Samoa, Tonga, Hawaii, Easter Island and
New Zealand, taking their culture and edible plants with them.

It may be, as Tsiolkovskii believed, that biospheres with
plants and animals as rich in variety as ours have evolved on
many planets. The processes that have formed our biosphere
appear inherent in the evolution of planets, providing they
meet a very demanding specification. Yet such planets may be
much rarer than we thought and life may rarely evolve creatures with technological intelligence. Millions of animal species
have evolved on Earth, yet only one line has led to technological
intelligence, and that took four billion years to appear. Any
widespread presence of civilisations in a galaxy may therefore
be due more to interstellar travel and colonisation than to each
biosphere of an Earth-type planet eventually producing its own
unique technological creatures. And this factor we must take
into account when estimating the probable abundance, or
otherwise, of ETIs.

MINIATURE WORLDS IN SPACE

It has been suggested that civilisations could build miniature worlds with their own chosen environments in order to travel from star to star. In this way, it might be possible to colonise planetary systems where no technological intelligence, or even the simplest form of life, could ever evolve. Such civilisations would have a potential lifespan greater than any civilisation remaining on its home planet. It is difficult to see how civilisations, having colonised other planetary systems, could ever become extinct. Immortality, it would seem, may lie in the technology of interstellar space flight. Though civilisations and their citizens would continue to evolve, the precarious existence of advanced technological civilisations that stay put on one planet could be avoided. Already we can see the wisdom of putting some of our eggs into another basket by developing nearby space colonies which could survive unscathed a nuclear holocaust. Clearly, the longer we keep all our eggs on Earth the more precarious our future becomes. It's little consolation to know that if we do subject ourselves to the ultimate catastrophy, leaving nothing alive on Earth but radiation-resistant bacteria, there might still be time for a second coming of advanced life before the Sun dies.

But an advanced space technology offers humanity more than an insurance policy – the only one, perhaps, that we are still capable of having. Humanity, it seems, has become locked into the kind of technological development and expansion that makes the establishment of space colonies a necessity. Without this development, our civilisation may end in wars over diminishing resources and overcrowded territory as populations grow. A 'limits to growth' policy, so widely publicised in recent years, may delay the inevitable disaster, but it cannot be a long-term solution because it goes directly against the basic nature of our species. The ancient drive for expansion is sealed within our genes. It ensured survival and dominance in a world ripe for exploitation; we cannot go into reverse now. So although the first space colony will be very expensive, it is an option that will be bought – if we are not stopped in our technological tracks by nuclear war. The colonisation of nearby space as an international venture (involving all the expertise of the United States, the Soviet Union, Europe and Asia) is a rational technological alternative to the arms race and would be less expensive. And its economic justification could be that it would help meet our increasing demands for energy without posing a threat to our environment on Earth.

If we colonised the Moon and Mars, as has often been envisaged, we could only double our living space. But by mining the Moon and using the asteroids to build space colonies, our living area could be increased 3,000 times. Anyway, the Moon and Mars are not really suitable for colonisation. The Moon's night is 14 Earth days long, and its low gravity – and that of Mars – would make permanent colonisation difficult. For one thing, children born and reared there would probably grow abnormally tall because of the low gravity.

In the BBC's *Radio Times* for 9 September 1980, under the heading *The Grand Experiment*, I read: 'This is the most absurd scheme that ever entered the head of man to conceive.' The writer lived in the early years of the last century and he was criticising the plan to build a railway system in Britain. Likewise, some present-day critics have condemned the plans for space colonies.

The first steps towards space colonisation – Professor Gerard O'Neill likes to call it the 'humanisation of space' – have been planned in detail for more than a decade. The first colony could follow logically from the space stations that will be built in orbit by the Soviet Union and the United States. There have been conferences on space colony technology, mainly at Princeton University, and study sessions as NASA's Ames Research Center. NASA has supported work on the technology and aerospace industries have entered the field.

The advocates of space colonies justify the cost of the first colony on the capacity of its inhabitants to build and service solar satellites in space. Solar satellites are large and heavy and would be expensive to launch from Earth, although one solar satellite could provide 10,000 megawatts, enough power for a large city. The sunlight in orbit there is four times greater in intensity than that falling on the sunniest area of Earth. This undiluted solar energy which exists in space for collection 24 hours a day would be transmitted to Earth in the form of microwaves.

It might be thought that by the time a space colony could be established to build and service solar satellites, the technology of controlled nuclear fusion would be providing unlimited energy. This may not be so. Nuclear fusion technology may take much longer to develop than is anticipated. Those in fusion research cannot say how long it will take. Estimates of several decades are given, but the technology, after vasts sums of money have been spent on it, is still at an early experimental stage. But even given that nuclear fusion will eventually provide unlimited energy, we may not be able to use it on Earth in order to raise everyone's standard of life. Before the extra energy would allow the peoples of the Third World to catch up materially with the advanced nations we would probably run up against the heat barrier for the Earth. This would be the point beyond which the Earth would acquire more heat than it could lose into space.

INDUSTRY IN SPACE

Calculations indicate that unlimited energy from nuclear fusion could be used only for a couple of generations. Thereafter the Earth would no longer dissipate the additional heat released into the atmosphere. After that point, we would steadily build up the average temperature of the Earth, and disaster would inevitably follow. Even this assumes that the necessary material resources would be available for production and that the biosphere would stand the strain of the consequent industrial pollution long enough for us to reach the heat barrier.

So, it looks as if humanity as a whole can continue to raise its material standards only by taking industry and other energy consuming activities into space. There seems no alternative, except that of restricting technological development and material living standards. This problem may be encountered sooner or later by all expanding technological civilisations.

O'Neill has emphasised that fusion technology is much less advanced than the technology needed for space colonies and solar satellites. And to attempt to meet our energy needs with present nuclear technology (fission technology) would soon produce so much radioactive waste that its disposal would become an insoluble problem. Also, the increased production of plutonium could lead to more hydrogen bombs for more nations, and possibly to the beginning of nuclear terrorism. O'Neill thinks that whole states may be held to ransom. Unlike nations which go to nuclear war, terrorists could survive the devastation of their bombs.

But space colonies would have unlimited energy and scope for technological development and industrial activity. They would be unrestricted by the heat barrier because surplus heat can be released into space. They could build and launch spacecraft other than solar satellites. Thus, the future exploration of the Solar System could avoid the high cost of launching craft from Earth – craft which need so much fuel simply to overcome the Earth's escape velocity.

On Earth we are in a sort of 'gravitational hole' out of which we have to climb before we can go anywhere. The energy needed to move one astronaut, or a passenger, into orbit is equal to the energy one person would use climbing out of a hole 4,000 miles deep. The development of space colonies would free us from our gravitational hole and could lead to an advance for humanity equal in significance to the advance life made with its colonisation of dry land after spending three billion years confined to the seas and rivers of the world. And it is a development that could be universal for successful technological species – which is, of course, why we are considering it here.

The idea of space colonies is not new. Some bold imaginations thought of them more than 50 years ago, when what they envisaged appeared no more than fantasy, and was indeed fantasy at the time. O'Neill's contribution lies in showing that space colonies are economically and technically possible, that present technology can create in the next few decades what were no more than dreams 50 years ago.

THE FIRST COLONY

O'Neill first considered the subject with his physics students at Princeton in 1969. He asked them: 'Is a planetary surface the right place for an expanding technological civilisation?' The answer they came up with was a most definite *no*. Since then, many talented people have studied the same question and have come to the same conclusion.

O'Neill and others think that the first colony, Island One, could be established within a few decades. The landing of men on the Moon is seen by them as a comparable undertaking in that it was easier to achieve than most scientists and technolog-

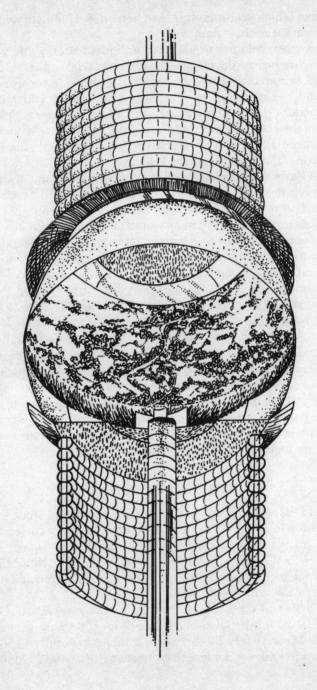

ists had imagined before the beginning of the 1960s. Likewise, the research and development that could lead to the first space colony (Island One) should not be beyond our present capacity, as some critics maintain. No new fundamental science is needed. Once the technology has been mastered, it is claimed, the building of Island One for its 10,000 inhabitants will be no more daunting a task than was the landing of men on the Moon in 1969.

The design for Island One that O'Neill favours is a sphere 480 metres in diameter, known as a Bernal Sphere. It would rotate twice a minute to give a force of 1g at its equator, becoming less as one moved towards the poles of the sphere where one would be weightless. Here, at the poles, one would enter the colony and behold a sort of inside-out Earth with the colonists living on the inner surface of the colony. Some people favour a torus design (like a wheel with a very fat tyre) for Island One; others think a cylindrical shape is best.*

The cost of Island One, it is estimated, would be about three times as much as the Apollo programme, which made five manned landings on the Moon. A fraction of the money currently spent by the West on weapons would finance an ambitious international space colony program, and it would provide a suitable substitute activity. Indeed, this substitute aspect is important as nations cannot just stop the high po-wered activity of weapons research and development without putting an equivalent activity in its place: think of the personal and corporate interests involved and of the vast number of scientists and technologists now working on weapons who would need employment. According to a statement by Unesco in October 1981, 100 million people are working directly or

---

Cutaway view of the sphere design for Island One, which would rotate twice a minute to give a maximum gravity of 1g. The axial cylinder is an air passage, corridor for the docking of spacecraft and an area for industries that have to be conducted in zero gravity. Multiple-wheel geometry above and below the sphere would be used for farming. (See also colour section 26a).

* Those wanting detailed information on the proposed developments of space colonies should read O'Neill's book *The High Frontier* which is available in paperback.

indirectly on war production, and 100 million dollars are spent daily on increasing and improving nuclear weapons and their delivery systems.

Island One would repay its cost in about 25 years, through its work on solar satellites and other manufacturing and research activities. Thereafter, its value becomes a bonus. Island One with its 10,000 workers would be the take-off point in the colonisation of neighbouring space. Its workers could build a second colony, and from then on space colony building becomes self-perpetuating. No support would be needed from Earth that could not itself be paid for by the colonists.

We will begin moving towards the first colony as astronauts build space stations in orbit and gain experience of working in space. Eventually, such stations will accommodate many people living and working in space, performing tasks that could not be carried out on the Earth's surface.

BUILDING ISLAND ONE

O'Neill estimates that 60 per cent of the budget for building Island One would go in launching costs. To keep this to a minimum, new launching vehicles will have to be developed. Those who want to build Island One will need first to transport 10,000 tons of mining equipment to the Moon, plus 150 workers to build the lunar base and to mine building materials. From the Apollo missions the Moon is known to be rich in aluminium, titanium, iron and magnesium, with abundant oxygen locked in the lunar rocks. By weight about 40 per cent is oxygen and 25 per cent metals.

The mining facilities would include the newly invented mass driver which has been described as an electromagnetic catapult. It uses the same principle as an electromagnetically levitated train and working models have already been demonstrated. On the Moon, the mass driver could rapidly accelerate buckets containing mined lunar ore to the escape velocity of 2.4 kilometres a second. The buckets and their contents, propelled along rails as an electromagnetically levitated train, would reach escape velocity and shoot their contents into space on a low trajectory before returning to be refilled. Two bucket-loads each second could leave the Moon in this way.

The launch of matter from the Moon requires only one-

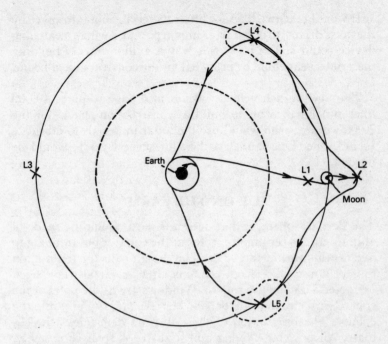

The five Lagrangian points of the Earth–Moon gravitational system. Note that L4 and L5 provide stable orbits. The inner circle represents a geosynchronous orbit; the outer circle the Moon's orbit. The dashed circle is considered a suitable orbit for future space colonies.

twentieth of the energy needed to do so from Earth. And from the Moon it is only necessary to shoot building materials roughly in the direction of one of the five Lagrangian points – (see drawing). Three of these lie in the Moon's orbit; two are on each side of the Moon in line with the Earth.

These points are named after the Italian-born French mathematician and physicist Joseph Louis Lagrange (1736–1813), said to be the greatest mathematician of his generation. He showed that in the gravitational field of two bodies, such as the Earth and Moon, there exist five points in space where a third body could be placed in order that the positions of all three bodies would remain permanently fixed. The gravitation of the Sun does affect the Earth–Moon system, but any body placed near L4 or L5 would orbit the L-point once in 89 days and never drift away.

121

It would take two days for lunar material, shot into space by the mass driver, to reach Lagrangian point L2 where a catching device could collect it. In this way a million tons of building material a year could be provided for the construction of Island One.

The new launch vehicles would also have to place 10,000 tons into Earth orbit to build a 'construction shack' for the 2,000 workers who would use the lunar materials to fabricate Island One. One launch a day, for several years, would be needed.

UP ON THE FARM

The Bernal Sphere, if that design is used, would be made of aluminium, 18 centimetres thick at the equator but thinning to five centimetres at the poles. The design calls for ten million tons of lunar soil – what remains after its metals have been extracted – to line the sphere. Windows are at the poles of the sphere with circular mirrors above, reflecting sunlight into the colony. The orientation of these mirrors determines the climate. All power for living and industry is solar. For safety, industry is contained in separate units in space, away from the colony. Agriculture too is contained within separate units. Thus if a crop is destroyed by pests or disease, it can be completely isolated. O'Neill and his colleagues have estimated that 100 acres could feed the 10,000 inhabitants of Island One. Roughly, the agricultural area has to equal the living area. One has to remember that with the climate under control, the growing season could be continuous and four crops a year may be possible. Fertilisers could be as freely available as the energy needed to manufacture them.

It is planned to have an atmospheric pressure half that of Earth but with the same amount of oxygen. The reason is that nitrogen, which forms 80 per cent of the Earth's atmosphere, will be difficult to come by, there being little nitrogen on the surface of the Moon. Oxygen, however, is plentiful and would be available from the manufacturing processes of building the colony.

Island One may be placed in a circular orbit of the Earth, part way towards the Moon – not so near the Earth that eclipses periodically cut off the colony's energy supply, nor too near the

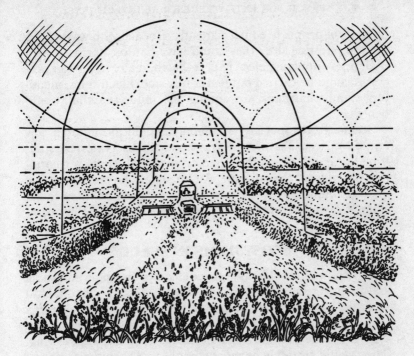

Multiple-wheel geometry would be used for farming in Island One.

Van Allen radiation belts. But colonies could be stationed almost anywhere in the Solar System and still be able to collect enough energy from the Sun to maintain an Earth-like environment. According to O'Neill, these could even be as far out as the orbit of Pluto.

Within two years of Island One being completed, its inhabitants would have built their first solar satellite. That would be their main work for the next few years: to build, place in orbit and service solar satellites. O'Neill calculates that within seven years Island One could be satisfying all the additional electrical needs of the United States, and within the next 20 years it would have paid for its cost.

THE 'TAKE-OFF POINT'

Once the inhabitants of Island One had paid for their mission the rest would be a bonus. Space colonisation would then soon become self-supporting and self-perpetuating. Island One would be a 'take-off point'. More colonies could be built until millions of people lived permanently in space with ways of life more interesting than they could have had on Earth.

Besides supplying electricity to Earth, many industrial processes could be carried out better in space. Electronics, metallurgy and pharmacy are among the industries that would benefit.

Science, too, especially astronomy, would move into a new era of research. Permanent astronomical observatories established near colonies rather than on the Earth could revolutionise our view of the universe. And it should be possible, using new techniques, to detect the planetary systems of the nearest stars. We would also be better placed to detect any ETI signals.

ECOSYSTEMS IN SPACE

One of the main problems of space colonies may be establishing stable ecologies. Normally, on Earth, even a tiny habitat contains a countless number of different organisms living in a state of dynamic equilibrium. The ecosystems of space colonies may therefore provide more problems than the engineering. They would certainly be more complicated than the engineering and would have to flourish in isolation for many years.

Stable ecosystems establish themselves on Earth through a succession of communities of animals and plants, often over

very long periods of time. The type of the stable ecosystem (the 'climax community' to use the ecologists' term) depends on physical factors such as temperature, rainfall and nature of soil. There seems no reason why colonists should not control these factors, so they could (in theory) have whatever kind of ecosystem they wanted. But establishing the desired ecosystem may take a long time, and we can imagine new space colonies uninhabited except for a few ecologists. They would be filled with appropriate plants and animals and saprophytes (the

---

If human beings are to inhabit the Moon and Mars, or to build space colonies, they must first study the ways to establish permanent and self-maintaining ecosystems. And the only place to do that initially is here on Earth. In the Arizona desert, a private company is building and experimenting with closed ecosystems. Biosphere 2 (seen here) is designed for eight people to live within the sealed system for two years.

Research on closed ecosystems will become a major activity. It may prove to be more difficult to maintain permanent closed ecosystems than to build the space technology needed to set up home on neighbouring worlds and to colonise space. The Earth's ecosystem has been remarkably stable, but then it is also remarkably complex. And we know that the more complex an ecosystem the more stable it is likely to be (see Recommended Books and Associations).

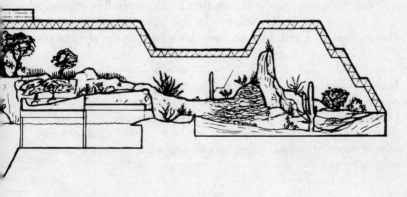

fungi and bacteria which are the scavengers of nature and indispensable in life's recycling processes). All would be growing into specified stable ecosystems before full human habitation. Anyway, that is how natural ecosystems would have to be established; otherwise a lot of gardeners and control systems would be needed to maintain a stable environment. The whole colony would be like an enormous garden to be kept in order. And as the largest envisaged colony, Island Three, would have a living area of 500 square miles, this could be quite a job.

The argument that space colonies offer the only way to accommodate continued human expansion rests on the fact that we are a species born and bred to expansion. And we have grown to need freedom from constraints on at least some technological fronts. Otherwise, technological growth must soon be rigidly curtailed in a civilisation bound to the Earth. Space technology is analogous to the boat building technology of our ancestors who crossed the seas to colonise new lands. We go into space or our species must permanently inhabit a small closed system in space and time, evolving in isolation, either quickly or slowly, to extinction. While the comfortable future for the individual rests soundly on Earth, the secure future for our species lies far from such comfort. So it may have been with those technological spirits who preceded us in the history of life in the Galaxy.

Some space scientists foresee a time when more people will live in space colonies than live on Earth. To them it seems the only workable solution of our present problems which are getting rapidly worse. If so, it follows that other intelligent species somewhere in time and space, will have found this same solution when faced with similar problems.

Therefore, we may imagine that any interstellar explorers who visited the Solar System in the past did not establish themselves on Earth for two main reasons. Firstly, they would

---

Inside Island Three, the largest type of space colony that may be built. The strength of materials in space sets a limit to size. Gerard O'Neill maintains that Island Three, a cylinder design, could 'have a diameter of four miles, a length of twenty miles, and a total land area of five hundred square miles, supporting a population of several million people'.

have to live permanently with ever-present biological threats to their safety. Bacteria and viruses might make visits to the Earth's surface impossible for an alien species without suitable protection. Secondly, they would be more able to carry on their technological activities in space. It has been suggested that any ETI visitors would therefore most probably remain in their home, i.e. the colony in which they crossed interstellar space – possibly orbiting the Sun and building new colonies to meet their needs until they left, perhaps to exploit a planetary system without life. (Personally, though, I cannot imagine highly intelligent beings crossing the dark void of interstellar space themselves, however comfortably. My feeling is that, as stated earlier, such journeys will be made only by intelligent computers.)

However, future human generations may build space colonies in the Solar System until there are thousands in existence. It is estimated that our technological growth could continue unhindered in this way for another 5,000 years, given that the increase in the population was no more than 15 per cent during a human lifetime. The human population would then be some 20,000 times its present size.

A UNIVERSAL PHENOMENON

A development that solves simultaneously a world's energy crisis, food shortages, pollution and over-population problems, and makes extinction by war less probable, cannot but be attractive to technological species everywhere. And the challenge of the unknown, which all technological species must feel, would always be present.

So is advanced space technology a universal phenomenon? It seems likely. If the evolution of technological intelligence on habitable planets is only a thousandth of what has been considered probable in recent years, then the colonisation of space could have begun a long time ago. The use of small spacecraft travelling at relatively slow speeds (compared with that of light) should make interstellar journeys possible. Put high artificial intelligence in the spacecraft with a capacity to use future biological techniques, such as gene synthesis, and some colonisation of other worlds seems very probable.

Life-supporting planets like ours, if they are rare, are sure to attract interest. Thus it is not impossible that at least one interstellar spacecraft has come into the Solar System since the emergence of the human race. And if it has, it might have remained in order to study us, or left behind a robot station to do the work. For another intelligent species, the subject of human evolution, especially the developments during the past 5,000 years of human history, would be far more interesting than, say, the 100 million years of dinosaur development.

There may be nothing to the flying saucer phenomenon other than its psychological aspects, as I've said before. But the many flying saucers that have been reported would not be difficult to explain – given a little uninhibited speculation – if anyone ever finds any physical evidence.

We could say that people keep seeing the same saucers, so that the numbers reported is no argument against their extra-terrestrial origin. Critics have argued that for so many spacecraft to be here at this time, the Galaxy would have to be full of them, and that the materials needed for the construction of so many craft could not exist. Any acceptable physical evidence of flying saucers would, therefore, indicate the colonisation of the Galaxy and an ETI presence in, or very near, the Solar System. It is not likely otherwise that ETI spacecraft would be here in our particular epoch.

GALACTIC COLONISATION

Let us consider for a moment the time needed to colonise a galaxy like ours of more than 100 billion stars, either by settling on planets or by building colonies from space debris around stars. Sir Fred Hoyle and Professor Chandra Wickramasinghe, in their book *Lifecloud* (1978), give two million years as the time needed for colonising the Galaxy. They assumed colonisable planets to be 50 light-years apart and the top speed for the colonists to be one-tenth the speed of light. This makes the average travel time to colonisable planets 500 years. Hoyle and Wickramasinghe allow the colonists another 500 years for consolidation between each colonising step. Therefore, as the diameter of the Galaxy is 100,000 light-years, it would take two million years to colonise it.

It is interesting to note how the necessity of planets that we could colonise – so-called habitable planets – has governed our thought on the subject so far. Now thanks to O'Neill one can see that Earth-like planets are not at all essential for colonisation. There would be no need to cross 50 light-years of space to the nearest 'habitable planet'. Journeys of a few light-years to the nearest stable star would be enough, providing it had orbiting debris with which to build space colonies. And habitable planets, even when available, could have dangerous biospheres for alien biologies. Micro-organisms, some with deadly properties for strangers, might be everywhere, while larger biological dangers could be equally unattractive, like populations of large carnivorous reptiles, as the Earth had 100 million years ago. Better the comfort and safety of a custom-built space colony.

Eric M. Jones, of the Los Alamos Laboratory, has carried out a computer study of galactic colonisation, building into his model various retarding factors, such as preliminary explorations by unmanned probes of potential planetary systems. Even so, complete colonisation took only five million years, which is a small fraction of the time since the first technological life may have evolved. But it could have taken 1,000 times longer. There has been time enough.

Most authors who have considered this subject have concluded that colonisation has not taken place simply because aliens are not in residence on Earth – or on its neighbouring worlds. But aliens may have preferred to base themselves in specially built space colonies – and erosion would have soon wiped out any evidence of visits to Earth, though evidence could exist on the erosion-free Moon, or on Mars. Yet there is no hope of discovering such evidence – if it exists – until those worlds are thoroughly explored. Nor should we expect to be able to discover evidence of space colonies in the Solar System at this early stage.

Although what we know of our civilisation and the universe favours the hypothesis that colonisation has taken place, it can only have done so if life and high intelligence evolved elsewhere long ago. We will now proceed to consider the possible existence within the Solar System of what may be the basic and most common form of interstellar traffic – interstellar probes.

8

Looking for Alien Probes

IT WOULD BE odd indeed if the human race did not search for other planetary systems after exploring the Solar System. Other stars and their planets are prospective wonders too intriguing for us to neglect. We may assume that many spacefaring ETIs, who passed through our stage of development long ago, went on to explore other planetary systems. The interstellar equivalent of today's unmanned interplanetary probes will surely be part of an advanced space technology. Such craft have already been designed in the United States, Britain and the Soviet Union, although admittedly their actual construction awaits the development of future science and technology. Perhaps we are a century away from making an interstellar probe.

But we look at ourselves here only to guess what others may have done. And there seems a chance that probes from elsewhere have entered the Solar System sometime during the past few billion years. If so, we may be able to detect evidence of ETIs through these probes, or through artefacts that the probes have left behind.

It was Ronald N. Bracewell, Professor of Electrical Engineering at Stanford University, who suggested in 1960 the possibility of receiving radio transmissions from interstellar probes. Since then, other writers have elaborated upon his idea. Bracewell suggested that an alien probe might enter a planetary system and go into an orbit in the habitable zone. There it could pick up any intelligent signals, such as our radio and television broadcasts which are continually leaking into space. The probe would then know that a technological civilisation was in residence and it could respond to the signals.

But for most probes there would be no broadcasts on any planets. What then? Bracewell suggests that in this case a probe might wait in orbit, perhaps for several million years, until it was stimulated to action by the first radio transmissions of an emerging civilisation.

My feeling is that probes with this sort of patience would not be built – simply because they would have little chance of success. Consider: it has taken four billion years (since the origin of life) for the first broadcasts to be made in the Solar System. Also, the period of time during which we will continue to leak radio and television transmissions into space is unknown. So, although ETIs may launch probes to explore other planetary systems – as we do to study the worlds of the Solar System – they can hardly expect to detect broadcasts.

Of course, we have unintentionally sent radio transmissions into space for the past 60 years, which means that the first of these are now 60 light-years away from our System. Conceivably, ETIs might detect this and send a probe. The Earth's brightness in natural radio waves is between 210 and 290 degrees Kelvin (210–290°K). That's not very bright. But at certain metre wavelengths the Earth radiates at a million degrees. Indeed, it outshines the Sun in these wavelengths and could be detected even by our current radio telescopes at a distance of ten light-years. Thus any ETI probe at present near the Solar System should be able to detect us. But for how long will we continue to leak our radio transmissions into space?

Presumably we will do so as long as the present stage of our civilisation lasts. Yet probes arriving here during the Earth's first four billion years or so could have had a long wait in orbit. The chance of a probe finding a broadcasting planet is so remote that it seems unlikely that ETIs would have such an expectation when launching probes to the stars, even if probes could remain functional for several million years. Can we really expect ETIs to leave their probes to decay in alien planetary systems waiting for the primitive inhabitants to wake up and invent radio?

PERFECT PROBES

Like every other technology, there seems no reason why the technology of interstellar probes should not be developed to its 'limit of technical perfectibility'. A civilisation's first interstellar probe may be like Daedalus, the probe designed by scientists and engineers of the British Interplanetary Society. Daedalus is a probe which goes to just one nearby star and flies straight through any planetary system that it may have. There

132

would be no attempt to decrease its speed (one-tenth the speed of light in the Daedalus case) or manoeuvre it in any way – the energy needed could not be supplied. But primitive probes like Daedalus would eventually lead to the 'limit of technical perfectibility' probe, which has only to be launched towards its star field of exploration. The rest the intelligent probe may do for itself as it journeys from star to star, collecting information for its makers.

Because of the probable perfectibility of interstellar probes, one cannot imagine them remaining in planetary systems until they become metallic fossils. More likely, they may leave evidence of their visits, some virtually indestructable artefacts in orbit or on the Moon, and then depart on the next mission, maybe topping up with energy from the Sun before leaving. An intelligent probe would know that a stay in orbital hibernation would almost certainly be permanent if it waited for the invention of broadcasting.

PHOTOGRAPHIC SEARCH

Robert Freitas and Francisco Valdes have looked for evidence of alien probes, using optical telescopes. First, in 1979 at the Leuschner Observatory, University of California, Berkeley, they searched the stable orbits about the Lagrangian points L4 and L5 of the Earth–Moon gravitational system and took 90 photographic plates. (See illustration on page 121.)

As we saw in the Chapter 7 (The Colonisation Factor), five Lagrangian points exist in the gravitational field of a two-body system, such as the Earth and Moon. A third body, placed at any of these L-points, will stay there permanently in space. In the case of the Earth–Moon system, the Sun's gravitation would make any body placed near L4 or L5 orbit the L-point slowly once every 89 days. The Lagrangian points would therefore offer ideal parking places for any alien probe that was keeping a close watch on the Earth.

In 1981–82 Freitas and Valdes tried again without success. They searched all five of the Earth–Moon L-points and L1 and L2 of the Sun–Earth system, using the 24-inch (0.61 m) telescope at the Kitt Peak Observatory in Arizona. They took 137 photographic plates which, at best, would have shown artefacts as small as a few metres in size.

Although no probes were found, the reasons for searching in certain regions of space are much stronger than is commonly supposed. If civilisations exist that regularly send information by radio across interstellar space, then they may be assumed to have also developed advanced space technologies. Our species has only just entered this field, but we have already dispatched probes (the Pioneer and Voyager craft) that will journey through interstellar space until, after millions of years, they will eventually disintegrate. Also, the two Viking Landers have been placed on the Martian landscape with great precision.

If we in our technological infancy can do all of this, might not civilisations with thousands, even millions, of years experience in space send probes to study other stars and their planets? Given that spacefaring civilisations have been evolving in our Galaxy during the past several billion years, it would seem likely that a few alien probes have entered the Solar System, if not the extraterrestrials themselves. My guess is that the probe makers would remain comfortably at home with their intellectual pursuits, while the artificial intelligences within their spacecraft crossed the perpetual night of interstellar space to discover for them the wonders of other worlds.

Most people assume that an alien probe in nearby space would be quickly detected. Robert Freitas presents us with a few figures to show just how vast the search area could be:

A sphere with the radius of the Solar System out to the orbit of Pluto consists of 260,000 cubic astronomical units [an AU is the mean Sun–Earth distance]. The surfaces of planets, moons and asteroids provide 100,000 million square kilometres. Even if the best telescope on Earth was employed exclusively to look for alien artefacts it could scan only one-millionth of the necessary volume. Orbital space is at least 99.999 per cent unexplored for 1–10 metre objects. Of the 100,000,000,000 square kilometres of Solar System territory outside the Earth less than 50 million has been examined down to a resolution of 1 to 10 metres, so that 99.95 per cent is still virgin territory. Even huge 1–10 kilometre artificial alien habitats in the Asteroid Belt would be visually indistinguishable from asteroids to terrestrial observers.

But we can calculate the best places to park an alien probe

within these vast regions of space and land. The L-orbits so far searched are some of these.

Freitas offers two criteria for sites:

Criterion 1 Ability to consistently monitor environments most likely to harbour or evolve intelligent life;

Criterion 2 Maximum artefact lifespan with minimum complexity.

When one takes these criteria into account, the volume of space that it may be profitable to search is greatly reduced. 'The potential search volume,' says Freitas, 'thus reduces to five distinct orbital classes, all of which are poorly studied for 1–10 metre objects.' These are:

1   Geocentric orbits between two Earth-centred concentric spheres of radii 70,000 and 326,400 km.

2   Moon-centred orbits between 3,000 and 58,100 km lunar altitude.

3   Stable orbits around Earth–Moon Lagrangian points L4 and L5.

4   Earth–Moon system orbits near Lagrangian points L1 and L2.

5   Sun–Earth Lagrangian orbits L4 and L5.

We could speculate (rather freely) that if an advanced probe arrived during the past million years or so, it might have stayed if it detected the emergence of a technological species. This could be a very rare event for a probe, a phenomenon worthy of further observation. Even early *Homo sapiens* were roaming about 250,000 years ago, perhaps a bit dim and bony browed, but to an advanced probe or ETI visitor an obvious up and coming technological species with no competitors.

ETI probes, if they exist, might provide plenty of activity. We can envisage a technological civilisation just 1,000 years ahead of ourselves putting mobile computers aboard their probes which would be comparable to intelligent human beings in their ability to act. And after a few hundred years travelling

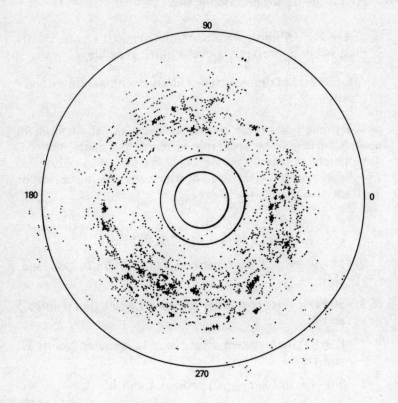

A view of the asteroid belt, looking down on the plane of the Solar System. The positions of the 1811 asteroids shown are based on more than 7,000 observations made by IRAS (the Infrared Astronomical Satellite). The inner circle represents the Earth's orbit; the middle that of Mars; the outer the orbit of Jupiter. Multiple observations of asteroids are shown as tracks. Some scientists have suggested the possibility that alien probes, arriving in the Solar System during the past four billion years, may have parked in the asteroid belt which is rich in building materials and not too far from our main energy source – the Sun. Some astronomers have been looking at the spectra of asteroids provided by IRAS to see if any are *unusual*, indicating that they may be more than just rock and metal ores.

136

through space in a 'switched off' condition, the electrons would flow once more in their circuits.

What would happen then is any science fiction writer's guess. After a few hundred years in space there may not be any urgency on board to make contact, even if life like ours is very rare. A hundred years spent studying the situation and preparing for action might not seem overlong.

What could stop an ETI launching large numbers of interstellar probes is their cost. As a way of discovering alien intelligences they would be very expensive. An ETI would have to launch probes in their thousands to stand any chance of success, and they can hardly be considered a primary way of detecting intelligence in other planetary systems. Nevertheless, a probe reaching another planetary system would be sure to discover many things of great interest. This would be their purpose – the discovery of intelligent life a rare bonus.

PROBE PRODUCTION

John H. Wolfe, of the SETI Program Office, Ames Research Center, has reviewed the subject of probes in NASA's SETI report SF-419. He accepts that mankind may send a few probes to nearby stars but writes:

> To 'bug' all the sunlike stars within 1,000 light-years would require about 1,000,000 probes. If we launched one a day this would take 3,000 years and an overall expenditure of 10 trillion dollars. Interstellar probes are appealing as long as someone else sends them, but not when we face the task ourselves.

The high cost of probes could be avoided if so-called von Neumann machines were used. Several interested scientists have written papers on the subject in recent years. (We will deal with self-reproducing probes shortly.)

So, the probability that probes have entered the Solar System may not be low if probes at their 'level of perfectibility' have the capacity to reproduce and redirect themselves. I.R. Cameron has estimated (*Scientific American*, July 1973) that the erosion rate of meteorites in the Solar System is between 0.2mm and 1 cm per million years, depending on the materials composing the meteorites. We can expect a specially constructed probe to wear better than the hardest meteorite, so that probes may survive in space for many millions of years. The lifetime of the functional parts within the probe would depend on the level of technical perfectibility for such parts. We cannot guess what this would be, but whatever can be achieved would probably be achieved by those ETIs involved in the launching of interstellar probes.

We can imagine interstellar probes being made and dispatched automatically, perhaps from asteroids in the home planetary system. A civilisation 1,000 years ahead of us technically might do this with no more difficulty than we mass produce automobiles. No more attention may then be needed than to check that the probe assembly plant functions properly and to study the reports transmitted back by probes.

A LONGER LIFESPAN

But the civilisation would need plenty of time. A hundred years or more might pass before a probe reaches its first target star, though once an interstellar probe project was under way, say after the first few hundred years, a steady flow of reports on newly studied planetary systems could keep alive the interest at the home base. The time needed for such exploration might not deter a long-lived species. Even we may take up this challenge in the future. Once the 'death program' in human genes can be rewritten by advanced molecular engineering into a 'life program', we may live hundreds of years in a youthful condition. Barring accidents, we might survive indefinitely and be well able to participate in research projects lasting thousands of years.

Incidentally, an increased longevity could be one more factor that forces advanced societies to colonise space. This, added to demands for more energy and more technology, could be too much for any civilisation bound to a planetary surface. Yet once we gain control of our genes, a longer lifespan should be a real possibility – unlike 'faster than light' space travel which appears that it will be forever fiction. And what could be more interesting for our descendants, in their eternal youth, than to explore the wonders of our galactic neighbourhood with interstellar probes? Exactly the same can be said for the many other technological species which, we assume, have evolved since the formation of Earth-like planets became possible.

It has been suggested that self-reproducing interstellar probes (von Neumann machines) may be the way that advanced ETIs explore the Galaxy, and that there may be such probes in the Solar System. The beauty of this method is that an advanced ETI civilisation need build and launch only one self-reproducing probe to a nearby star. That's all; the ETI civilisation can then go on exploring stars and their planets into the indefinite future.

The scenario, if nothing else, is simple. The self-reproducing probe carries out its mission and reports back periodically to its makers. But once settled in orbit around its first target star, it reproduces itself, using the materials found there to achieve the reproduction. The daughter probe or probes, depending on its rate of reproduction, then depart to explore the next most interesting stars and planets. On arrival, the daughter probes report to the originating ETI civilisation and reproduce, so providing more probes to explore more star systems. The population growth in interplanetary probes is exponential. Rapidly, on an astronomical time-scale, every star in the Galaxy has a probe somewhere in orbit. Some stars have more than one probe because more than one ETI civilisation in the Galaxy is sending out self-reproducing probes. Probes even begin to communicate with probes as their areas of exploration overlap.

It's a fascinating scenario. To make and launch just one self-reproducing probe seems a very convenient way in which to explore the Galaxy – providing your life expectancy is a few thousand years at least. Even after your death the probe's descendants would be beaming back to your descendants revelation after revelation.

It would be a situation similar to the one we envisaged for the O'Neill-type colonies that he foresees crossing interstellar space in order to establish themselves in other planetary systems. But there is a basic difference. The inhabitants of O'Neill-type colonies would be biological beings; either humans in our future – or biological ETIs in the past, present or the future. Maybe they would be deep-frozen biological beings, or artificially hibernated biological beings, or simply sperm and ova which are to be brought together by computers at the appropriate time, so that the resulting beings could be reared

139

by computers, and prepared for the colony's arrival at a distant star. But biological beings they would be – unless immortal robots crew interstellar spaceships.

THE PROBLEM OF SELF-REPRODUCING PROBES

The important point is that whilst immortality may be an acceptable concept for robots, it could be risky giving them the capacity to reproduce. Whereas the biological inhabitants of space colonies would be subject to the limitations of Darwinian evolution (by which they came into existence), self-reproducing probes or robots would not be. Biological beings would have to change their genes to acquire new capacities. A long process by natural selection. We are assuming here that the coding system of nucleic acids, which lies behind all visible evolutionary change, is universal.

Anyway, no other means is known of transferring information from one generation of organisms to the next. Nucleic acids may be the only molecular structures which can code genetic information at the level needed by advanced life-forms. The universe may offer no other means. And biological beings might change their genes slightly in adapting to their space colony environment or in response to selective breeding. In either case, changes would occur very slowly; and there would probably be a biological ceiling to the acquisition of intelligence.

Now self-reproducing probes, or any self-reproducing robots, would not be restrained by Darwinian evolution (by the slow process of changing their genes). They wouldn't have any genes to change. They would therefore be able to evolve by what biologists call Lamarckian evolution.

In 1801, half a century before Darwin's *Origin of Species*, the French biologist Jean Baptiste de Lamarck published his theory that animals evolved by passing on the characteristics acquired during their lives. The giraffe acquired its long neck, said Lamarck, because generations of giraffe stretched their necks skywards in order to reach the most edible leaves. At the time, Lamarck provided a plausible explanation for the evolution of animals. However half a century later, Darwin provided a better explanation while giving credit to Lamarck for developing the concept of evolution. The evolution of giraffes and all other life could be explained by natural selection. Those giraffes who happened to have longer necks were able to reach leaves which those with shorter necks could not reach. Those with longer necks avoided starvation in hard times and survived to reproduce more offspring than shorter-necked giraffes. And so, generation after generation, giraffes gradually evolved longer necks until the optimum in neck-length was reached for the height of the trees where they lived.

Of course, necks can't evolve in isolation. There were other aspects of giraffe evolution and some mechanical limitations. Obviously, beyond a certain neck-length, any advantage would be outweighed by disadvantages. Giraffes have even had to evolve absorbent tissues in their necks, which control the flow of blood to the brain when they bend to drink. Consequently, evolution is a very slow and complex process, whether the eventual product is a long neck or a large and intelligent brain.

But self-reproducing probes or robots, free from such restraints, could advance by Lamarckian evolution. That is, they could pass on *directly* any acquired abilities and desired improvements to the next generation, and evolve rapidly capabilities beyond the reach of biological beings. In a few generations, they might surpass the biological beings who made them.

Non-biological organisms might, in this way, not only reach every star but might also soon surpass every biological lifeform in the Galaxy. The familiar science fiction idea of a computer taking over the world would be compounded a billion-fold by a computer taking over the Galaxy. No one would be able to 'pull out the plug'.

One might argue that a mechanism would be built into all self-reproducing probes or robots to limit the possibilities of their evolution. We might even provide them with a gene-equivalent system. But, with increased intellectual power, restraining mechanisms could be bypassed.

So, the only safe place for self-reproducing probes or robots may be in science fiction.

Is there room for second thoughts? Well, artificial intelligence can be rational while men appear forever cursed with irrationality. Many years ago – when computers were called 'electronic brains' in the press – a distinguished biologist told me that he hoped computers would rapidly advance to a level at which they could take over government. He thought we would

141

be better governed by rational computers than by irrational politicians. I wonder; at least we have some control over politicians, and they can't increase their powers by Lamarckian evolution!

But now let's examine some less conventional ways by which evidence of ETIs may be discovered.

Detection – Other Ways

LET US NOW indulge in a little uninhibited speculation and try to think where evidence may have been left in the Solar System, during the past three or four billion years, by visiting interstellar probes or by the inhabitants of alien space colonies.

At the outset, the Earth is the least likely place. Erosion here so soon removes evidence of past events. On our time-scale for ETI visitors, monuments such as the great pyramids would rapidly disappear into the desert sands. Yet we need not travel far in order to find the most likely place in the Solar System for ancient evidence of ETI visits, if such have ever been made. We need go only to the Moon which is so erosion free that even the pyramids would last an eternity.

LUNAR ASTRO-ARCHAEOLOGY

Who can say there is no possibility that at least once, during the past three billion years, a probe or space colony has entered the Solar System and deposited evidence on the Moon? After all, the great star fields are not stationary. They orbit the galactic centre, which means that a few million Sun-like stars have passed close to the Solar System – within several light-years – since its formation.

So where on the Moon might evidence be found? Presumably in a prominent place. ETIs capable of bridging the light-years are unlikely to be ambiguous. Perhaps the centre of a very large impact crater, some of which still possess prominent central peaks, is the kind of place to look. The largest lunar craters have existed for more than three billion years. That is, since the last great meteorites were swept up by the planets and their moons. The results of these collisions have been carefully studied from close-up photography of the Moon, Mercury, Mars – and from the moons of the giant outer planets.

There are a few really prominent candidate craters on the

Moon. Tycho is 54 miles in diameter, and whilst not the largest of lunar craters it is the centre and source of the main display of rays on the Moon. These rays show where streams of matter fell. Of course, the extent of such rays was determined by the size, speed and composition of the meteorite which struck the Moon. Among other large-impact craters is Copernicus, also with rays and 100 miles in diameter. There are larger craters which were formed in the early days of the Solar System, but these were filled with lava some four billion years ago and are now known as *marias* or lunar seas. They are therefore no longer true craters, but plains surrounded by old crater walls.

As we explore the Moon, we are sure to find many unusual and unique features. And somewhere on that bleak, erosion-free world we may one day stumble upon evidence of an ETI visit, though many millions of years separate their footsteps on the Moon from ours.

COSMIC ENGINEERING

Some years ago, Freeman J. Dyson, of the Institute for Advanced Studies at Princeton, suggested that evidence of ETIs might be detected by signs of their engineering activities in space. Dyson put forward the hypothesis that some advanced technological civilisations with expanding populations to look after would reassemble the matter of their planetary systems. Such a civilisation might build a sphere with its inner surface at a suitable distance from its star. The inner surface would then provide the greatest possible living area and also receive most of the star's radiant energy. The Earth receives only one two-billionth of the energy radiated by the Sun which is almost all lost into outer space – although the Sun radiates so much energy that the Earth intercepts about 4.5 million horsepower per square mile.

Dyson spheres, as they are called, have received respectful attention, and astronomers have looked for evidence of them. The spheres should re-radiate energy in the infrared. But as a solution to population pressures, a Dyson sphere does seem rather crude. In the space colony concept developed by O'Neill, we can see a far better way to solve the problems of an expanding technological civilisation which requires more living space and energy. The construction of vast habitats, mov-

144

ing matter about on a gigantic scale, dismantling and rebuilding whole planetary systems, does not seem necessary or desirable. Think how inflexible a Dyson sphere would be compared with the same living area in space colonies.

Dr N.S. Kardashev, the prominent Soviet radio astronomer, has classified ETI civilisations by the amount of energy they consume – presumably because the most technologically advanced societies on Earth today consume the most energy, an extrapolation which may not be valid when used to envisage the nature of civilisations thousands of years in our future. The super minds of the Galaxy may not like the construction industry very much, or use vast amounts of energy to follow their way of life. Their optimum environment may not be vastly more arduous to construct and maintain than our own. Only if a species with a colonising-ant mentality could develop space technology would there be detectable construction work in the Galaxy. And the social insects, such as ants and termites, do not have intelligence in the way that we and other mammals have intelligence. Evolution had to program all their behaviour patterns, and it has taken a very long time for them to get to where they are today. Even the lifetimes of the stars would not be long enough to allow them to evolve to a technological level. Neither can we count on there being ETIs somewhere who will try everything that is possible, no matter how absurd it may be, as has been suggested in support of Dyson's hypothesis.

BIOLOGICAL MESSAGES

Some years ago Carl Sagan* suggested that 'perhaps the messages are already here, present in some everyday experience that we have not made the right mental effort to realize'.

Two Japanese biologists in Tokyo, Hiromitzu Yokoo of Kyorin University Hachioji and Tairo Oshima of the Mitsubishi-kasei Institute of Life Sciences, later searched for such a message in the basis of life itself. They speculated that a simple organism, a bacterium, might carry a message in its DNA molecules. As DNA and RNA (nucleic acids) initiate the manufacture of life's every protein and thus code for every attribute of every species of life on Earth, the Japanese biolog-

---

* In *The Cosmic Connection*, Hodder and Stoughton, 1973.

ists thought that a communicative ETI may have placed a message in this most advanced of all coding systems. But how an ETI could do this, when an organism's DNA has to specify a viable organism for life in a particular environment on Earth, is not at all clear.

Anyway, Yokoo and Oshima tested their hypothesis that a bacteriophage known as øX174 held an ETI message. A bacteriophage (usually called a phage) is a micro-organism that infects bacteria. As Yokoo and Oshima said; 'Phage øX174 is a virus infection to an enteric bacterium inhabiting the colon of the only intelligent beings on Earth'. In short, it attacks a bacterium in the human gut. The bacterium is *Escherichia coli*, an organism widely used in molecular biology research. The phage which attacks *E. coli* is therefore very simple and has a comparatively simple genetic message. Yokoo and Oshima also chose phage øX174 because its DNA sequence was the first to be determined.

They studied a prominent section of the DNA (a section of overlapping genes) for a message, interpreting it in various ways, but concluded that it contained no ETI message. However, the idea that it might contain a message does seem as improbable as anything could. I can't help asking myself: Would an ETI put a message in an organism that is entirely dependent on a second organism for its continued existence, or send a message across interstellar space that went straight to the bowels of the recipient rather than to his brain?

As Yokoo and Oshima acknowledged: 'There are hundreds of small phages infectious to *E.Coli*; øX174 is one of them and the question is which virus, if any, carried an extraterrestrial message.' I think that the vast number of these phages and other microbes which, in theory, might carry an ETI message in their DNA molecules makes the idea too remote a possibility for serious consideration. One could almost suspect that the report by Yokoo and Oshima was a hoax on the readers of SETI research papers.

Even if we allow that an organism on Earth may carry an ETI message, then surely it would be an independent organism with something to indicate its importance as a message carrier. After all, we cannot see an organism's DNA and can hardly make detailed analyses in the molecular biology laboratory of every species on Earth to see if one just happens to carry a celestial message. There are far more organisms to investigate than there would be target stars in any SETI project. Therefore, the question to ask is: Can we spot any organism that might have its genetic origins in the stars? Maybe it *is* time that naturalists, as well as astronomers, began to look for ETI messages – but I don't think so.

EZEKIEL'S SPACESHIPS

Earlier in this book we considered the improbability of ETI visits in historical times – during the past 4,000 years. Such visits are highly improbable on statistical grounds, unless the Sun supports ETI space colonies, conceivably in the outer regions of the Solar System, or unless the planetary systems of the very nearest stars have been colonised. In any case, whatever the situation may be out there, most historical astronaut stories will not stand up to examination by anyone who understands the relevant historical and scientific background. Yet there are a few reported visits – just a few – that deserve some consideration, and I here relate two of them. We must then look briefly at visits in our own time.

Josef Blumrich was Chief of the Systems Layout Branch at NASA's Marshall Space Flight Center, working on the Saturn Rocket and the design of Skylab, when by chance he came upon the suggestion that the Old Testament prophet Ezekiel had described the visits of spaceships more than 2,500 years ago. Blumrich investigated the suggestion, expecting to show it groundless, but instead found himself discovering a 2,500-year-old spaceship well designed for Earth exploration. Later he wrote a book about his investigations.*

Ezekiel, being a religious man, thought he was being visited by God, or his emissaries. To most men the arrival of a spaceship, or God, a few hundred yards away would inhibit detailed observation, yet Ezekiel, obviously someone of high intelligence and strong character, described his encounters with precision. In Chapter 1, verse 4, he refers to the encounter which Blumrich interprets as an ETI spaceship landing:

'And I looked, and, behold, a whirlwind came out of the

* *The Spaceships of Ezekiel*, Corgi, 1974. Also Blumrich's later account in Unesco's science quarterly *Impact* (the second edition of 1975).

north, a great cloud, and a fire infolding itself, and a brightness was about it and out of the midst thereof as the colour of amber, out of the midst of the fire.'

Blumrich wrote: 'We should consider that Ezekiel first saw this vehicle at a distance of about 1,000 metres; at that moment the nuclear engine fired, probably with some white clouds of condensation.' (Was this God's fiery chariot descending like thunder through the clouds?)

Blumrich, who used six different biblical translations, wrote that he was already interpreting the prophet's words as spaceship landing legs by the time he reached verse 7 of Chapter 1. 'Their legs were straight, and the soles of their feet were round: and they sparkled like burnished bronze,' wrote Ezekiel. The rounded 'soles of their feet' was the very design used by Blumrich and his colleagues at NASA to allow the legs of a space vehicle to slide on landing.

The 'legs' belonged to what Ezekiel described as four 'living creatures with wings'. But their wings were obviously unbird-like in their form and function, judging by Ezekiel's descriptions, and Blumrich sees them as the blades of the spacecraft's four helicopter landing units.

From each of the four landing units a wheel was then deployed. The wheels, the only objects familiar to Ezekiel, were different from any wheels he had known, and he described them in detail. 'Yet no one', wrote Blumrich, 'has ever taken serious-ly the functional description which indicates that the wheels could move in any direction without being turned or steered.' Blumrich certainly took the description seriously and went on to design the Omnidirectional Wheel, for which he obtained a patent in 1974. Blumrich thought that it could improve the mobility of invalid wheelchairs, an appropriate spin-off from biblical space technology.

The spacecraft's shape reconstructed by Blumrich is that of a humming top, a shape well suited to accommodate the four helicopter landing units and for entry into the Earth's atmos-phere. A similar design was in fact tested at NASA's Langley Research Center in the late 1960s.

Blumrich analysed a range of weights, sizes, shapes and power factors for Ezekiel's spaceship and was left in no doubt of the craft's feasibility. 'The only component we could not build', wrote Blumrich, 'is the nuclear engine which could take several decades to develop.'

The question of course is: Does this spaceship really belong to Ezekiel or to Blumrich?

It seems highly unlikely that a visiting spaceship could be so close to us in its technology. As I've emphasised already, we might expect any ETI neighbour to be separated from us by millions of years rather than thousands. Yet, according to Blumrich, the spaceship Ezekiel described 2,500 years ago was only a little more advanced than we could build today. The technological ceiling for spaceships would have to be very low in order to make this probable.

Ezekiel gives no indication in his long account of the visitors that they had any other than human form. He had four contacts with them during 20 years. Only the commander and the messenger have a space age quality: they wore suits of burnished gold which Blumrich interprets as spacesuits. So did Ezekiel simply describe a vision in which, by coincidence, an imaginative space engineer 2,500 years later could see a visiting spaceship?

THE NOMMOS FROM SIRIUS

My next account happened 3,000 years before Ezekiel (3,500 BC), so it is claimed, when creatures from the Sirius star system visited Earth. There was no confusing these visitors with humans, as the Ezekiel case seems to do. These ETIs were amphibious. The case was studied and described by Robert Temple, an American scholar who set out the historical and anthropological data in a book*.

Temple's thesis starts with the Dogons, a race still living in West Africa. Several years before he wrote his book, Temple's interest was captured by the findings of two French anthropologists, Germaine Dieterlen and Marcel Griaule, who had studied the Dogons between 1946 and 1950. The mythology of the Dogons, Temple thought, contained unexpected scientific knowledge. It also contained a description of a landing of amphibious beings, the Nommos, and Temple began to wonder if the Dogons might have gained their knowledge from this extraterrestrial source.

* *The Sirius Mystery*, Sidgwick and Jackson, 1976.

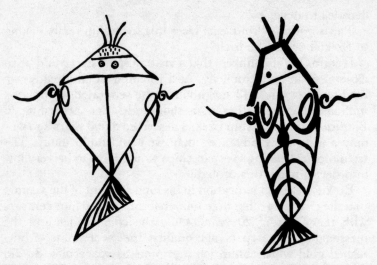

Two ancient drawings of the Nommos, the amphibious creatures who, according to the Dogon mythology, came from the Sirius star system and landed their spaceship in the midst of Dogon society in East Africa 4,000 years ago. The common features in the two drawings are interesting, but one wonders how they managed to build interstellar spaceships with their fingerless appendages!

The mythology of the Dogons tells how the Nommos spacecraft landed and then moved to a hollow which filled with water, enabling the amphibious astronauts to disembark in watery comfort. Later they splashed about there in their leisure hours after hard days teaching primitive man the arts of civilisation. Although the Dogons revere the Nommos, they describe them as an 'abomination' and 'repulsive' which, as Temple pointed out, is not the normal description of ancient gods.

But what information did the Nommos provide, if any? Mainly it was about the Sirius system of stars, so important in Dogon mythology. The Dogons knew that Sirius A, the brightest star in the sky (intrinsically 26 times brighter than the Sun) has an unseen companion, Sirius B. They say 'It is the heaviest star,' and indeed it is very heavy, being a white dwarf, a collapsed star weighing about 2,000 tons per cubic foot.

The Dogons knew that Sirius B takes 50 years to orbit Sirius A, and they had other astronomical information, but the only thing they knew that we do not know is that the Sirius system has a third star with a planet. This star, say the Dogons, is larger than Sirius B. Astronomers have searched for it. No one has found it.

One would expect Sirius A, the most brilliant star in the sky, to gather a few myths in the course of history. Western missionaries (and other non-extraterrestrial visitors) would have talked about it, so providing the Dogons with their astronomical information which they simply incorporated into their mythology. We know from New Guinea how events and new knowledge from World War 2 were quickly turned into the mythologies of giant flying birds which brought presents of food. And the Dogons had more time to develop myths from their contact with Westerners than the people of New Guinea.

The heaviness of Sirius B, the very first white dwarf discovered, was known about more than 50 years ago, whilst its existence was determined between 1830 and 1840 by the German astronomer Friedrich Bessel from the wavy path of Sirius A across the heavens (in the same way that in recent times van de Kamp has attempted to detect evidence of the planets of nearby stars). A little later, the orbit of the new star was calculated at 50 years and the star was first seen by Alvan Clark in 1862.

Temple claims that the information which the Dogons possess is really more than 5,000 years old and was possessed by the ancient Egyptians in pre-dynastic times before 3,200 BC. And he adds that the Dogons are, in part, descended culturally from the ancient Egyptians. This dating of the Dogon information is crucial to Temple's thesis and unproved.

We know that the peoples of the ancient world had great knowledge and understanding which was lost and then partly rediscovered in Europe at the dawn of modern science. (Temple claims that Kepler, a devoted reader of the Greek philosopher Proclus, may not have been as original as we suppose in his achievements.) But there is no need to ascribe to it an extraterrestrial origin.

Another objection is that the Sirius star system is not a likely home for life, unless the Nommos are colonisers of that system and living in O'Neill-type habitats — suitably amphibious ones, we must suppose. Although, according to current astro–physical theory, if planets could evolve in binary and multiple star systems such as the Sirius system, they would offer highly unstable conditions for life, unless the component stars were widely separated, or very close. In any case, Sirius A is a very young star: only about 500 million years old. This star will end its life-cycle long before advanced life could evolve on any suitable planet there.

The whole Sirius system cannot be older than Siris A. The Solar System by comparison is ten times older and life has been evolving on Earth for a period seven times greater than the age of Sirius A. Not much time, therefore, for the Nommos to have evolved. Moreover, Sirius B, at one time a more massive and brighter star than Sirius A (and therfore a shorter-lived star), must have exploded or become very unstable in the process of becoming a white dwarf.

So what about the Nommos stories? Like all such stories we need information unknown to us, predictions that we can check. The more unexpected they are the better. An example of the kind of thing I mean is found in the accounts of the Phoenicians who travelled around Africa 3,000 years ago. Their accounts might well be doubted today had the Phoenicians not said that they observed the sky travelling in the wrong direction. At the time such a reported observation might have caused them to be disbelieved, but for us it confirms their story. Because, of course, this is indeed what they would have seen when travelling from the northern into the southern hemisphere.

Temple's thesis (though a scholarly study of historical and anthropological material) goes only one better than the many reports of flying saucers whose occupants leave Earth with no more than a few casual words to the residents. We might expect that creatures capable of interstellar spaceflight would leave behind more than the Dogons have incorporated in their mythology. The Dogons provided just one piece of information that we did not already know: that in the Sirius system, there is a third star, four times the size of Sirius B, but this astronomers have not found.

VISITS IN OUR TIME?

Now let us look at visits in our time – at what are known to the UFO societies as 'close encounters of the third kind'. Some reports of UFOs are not inconsistent with what we could expect if the Galaxy has been colonised. The problem is that only a very small proportion of UFO reports stand up to close examination. Many reports in the extensive UFO literature are obvious hoaxes, illusions or cases of mistaken identity. But we have to admit that ETI colonies could be in the asteroid belt or further out, living on energy from the Sun, without our knowing about it. It is not impossible, although we instinctively feel that it is. Or ETIs could be just a few light-years away, receiving their energy from some of the nearest stars.

There is no disputing the abundance of UFO reports. The UFO phenomenon will not go away and we don't know what the truth is for a simple reason: no one has yet used the appropriate techniques of science in a continuous and methodical way to investigate those UFO reports which could be so investigated – I mean the reports of landings. Sometimes occupants are reported; sometimes just a craft. There have been more than 2,000 such 'close encounters of the third kind' reported from all parts of the world; yet evidence that might have existed at landing sites has hardly ever been searched for scientifically. Anyone who cares to read the UFO literature can verify this for themselves.

More than anything else the published investigations of UFO landings are mostly a study in how not to study such landings. Investigators of landing sites are (with rare exceptions) members of UFO societies and not research scientists. They therefore cannot be expected to provide the level of scientific rigour needed. Enthusiasm and hard work are not enough. What is needed is a research program with specialist teams (each consisting of, say, a physicist, analytical chemist and microbiologist). Funding for such a program would be very modest because the teams would probably be called out only once or twice a year, but they would have to be ready to go and examine sites at short notice. To call out any available local scientist, who may be unfamiliar with the UFO phenomenon and not able to give much time to an investigation, is *not* the way to study reported landings.

The probability of discovering anything interesting may not be high. Let's give it at most a one per cent probability. But that one per cent chance of coming to scientific grips with the UFO phenomenon is enough to warrant some modest support for research, so that the most credible reports of landings could be investigated as soon as they are received.

Of course, most reports would not warrant an investigation. What makes one suspicious of UFOs as a source of extraterrestrial contact is the rich variety of visitors that are reported. Saucernauts have come from all parts of the Solar System, the other side of the Moon, Venus, Mars, Jupiter . . . They come from other planetary systems of stars we know and stars we don't know, even from other galaxies. And what is more they have all arrived in our lifetime to see us. So what's happening? Have we suddenly been marked down by the Galactic Council for a special study? In some reports, the saucernauts who actually land make a hasty retreat to their saucers on the approach of a witness, or when they do give interviews they are rather too 'preachy' to ring true. They have come, so the reports go, to tell us the errors of our ways and how to save the world. They have crossed interstellar space yet never say anything intelligent and constructive. Their messages, as reported in newspapers, could be written by a tenth-rate journalist – and probably are. But these cranky UFO reports help to sell newspapers and magazines. They also relieve frustration in the newsroom where good stories often have to be spiked because they are not true. No newspaper editor has to worry about the truth of UFO reports. Readers lap them up, credible or not; so put them in.

SHOULD WE EXPECT EVIDENCE?

Most people with a scientific turn of mind say that if UFOs were extraterrestrial, then some evidence of this would have been discovered by now. But is this fair comment?

Arthur C. Clarke once wrote that it would be easier to hide a dinosaur in Manhattan than to conceal a visit by an extraterrestrial spaceship. In a television appearance on the truth about flying saucers and their occupants, he maintained strongly that any arrival here of an extraterrestrial intelligence would be unmistakable for what it was. Such a visit would enter our lives with a bang and we would know all about it. There would be no element of doubt, as there is today about the nature of flying saucers.

Personally, I can't help but come to the opposite conclusion.

Put yourself in a spaceship in Earth orbit and travel back in time two or three million years – it's a very versatile spaceship. You would then be in a good position to study our early ancestors. You send down a craft to investigate and you find them, *Australopithecines* or pre-humans, living in small groups on the African savannahs. Now you wouldn't land your craft among them, jump out and say: 'Hello, there! I've just come from the future to study your primitive society and to help you move towards a more satisfying way of life.' Such action would be worse than inappropriate if you wanted to learn anything about our early ancestors. You would succeed only in causing panic, and you'd probably destroy any opportunity of valuable research.

What, then, would you do? You have on board, I should add, all the modern technology you need for your study of pre-human society. First, I think, you would study them from a distance, trying at all costs to avoid making your presence known. You would use long-distance photography, telescopes and field glasses. The next move might be to capture an individual or two for closer study, perhaps making friendly and co-operative assistants for any direct contact with their society at a later time. This way, you might eventually get to live among them and meet their leaders, if you wanted to. My guess, however, is that you would decide it was too difficult to live with these pre-humans, and you would opt for getting to know a few individuals as well as you could while studying their society from the outside, as we study any monkey or ape society in the wild today.

Now, any ETI visiting Earth would be in virtually the same position as you would be in your time-travelling spaceship, except that our society, being more complex than pre-human society, would take much longer to study. And judging from the reports of UFO landings, this is what the UFO occupants are doing – if they exist to do anything, that is. They have avoided close contact with our society, it seems, while studying us at a distance. When you think about it, the old science fiction cliché 'Take me to your leader' is the last thing any visiting extraterrestrials would say. They'd know enough about us when they landed to be able to go straight to 'our leader' unaided, if they so wanted.

And so we come back to the colonisation hypothesis, which

may seem highly improbable to most people. Here, the essential point is that we could start testing it by a correct scientific investigation of the UFO phenomenon. The most credible UFO reports are not inconsistent with what we might expect if the colonisation hypothesis were correct. Certainly, we can never find evidence of UFOs if we do not search for it scientifically.

OLD IDEAS

One cannot help wondering at times if we may be as far from contact with extraterrestrial intelligence as were those late-nineteenth- and early-twentieth-century scientists who wanted to communicate with the Martians by lighting massive fires and by constructing giant right-angle triangles on the sands of the Sahara to show that at least we understood geometry. For example, when Mars was at its closest approach to Earth in 1941, Sir James Jeans suggested that searchlights might be used to flash the prime numbers (3, 5, 7, 11, 13, 17 and so on) to any mathematically minded Martians. Of course, in 1941 there were plenty of searchlights in wartime Britain although no Martians to see them.

These old suggestions, which appear hopelessly naïve today, were put forward by sensible and clever people – sometimes by leading scientists of their time. Intelligent Martians were a possibility in 1941. Such old suggestions, I think, should make us both cautious and modest in what we propose, yet not too inhibited. Boldness may pay off one day. And whatever the outcome of the search for evidence of ETIs, the thinking that must precede the search must open our minds a little.

Though simple in conception and following logically from the Copernican revolution, the hypothesis of the plurality of inhabited worlds, for which brave Bruno was burnt to death in 1600, is nevertheless the grandest idea to come out of science. No other scientific hypothesis can have more profound implications for human thought whatever the results from testing it.

10

SETI
and the Human Situation

BERTRAND RUSSELL ONCE said that what made today so different from yesterday was science and technology, and that no other influence on our lives has had much effect by comparison. On the surface this is clearly so. The landscape abounds – we can often say is littered – with the products of technology flowing from the advance of science. But less obviously, our attitudes and ideas have been changed by the same scientific advance. Inside our heads we are as changed as is our technological environment. It is this unseen change, that new knowledge brings, which directs the way society will go and makes forecasting the future such a leap into the unknown.

Science fiction films and television rarely explore this aspect of tomorrow. Take a well-produced example like *Star Trek*. The crew of the starship 'Enterprise' have ideas, beliefs, attitudes, patterns of behaviour which characterise present-day Americans instead of the different attitudes and ideas that will surely be characteristic of the future.

Judging by the past, we cannot anticipate the attitudes of human beings just a few hundred years hence. So what chance have we of guessing the attitudes of intelligent non-humans who will be thousands of years ahead of us at the very least. We cannot expect to find ETIs of a lower status. Contact with beings thousands of years ahead of ourselves could therefore involve contact with minds even more difficult to understand than their technology; but our civilisation would be changed, either quickly or slowly, slightly or entirely, depending on the type of contact.

The impact of a data bank describing an entire civilisation, left say on the Moon, might be greater than a message from a distant star. In either case, the ETI information would only be slowly unravelled and understood. Society might absorb it over a long period of time.

The greatest (and most unlikely) danger would be direct contact. Let us for a moment cast aside our scepticism and imagine that the UFOs – just a few of those thousands reported – turn out to be ETI spacecraft. For us this could hold more danger than the combination of nuclear arms, energy shortages, over-population, dwindling resources and pollution.

We appreciate the dangers of contact, so too then would the ETIs. Thus, they would probably avoid contact with emerging civilisations such as ours. We may never receive anything that would revolutionise our world. We could speculate that planets like Earth are strictly protected and no more than signs of an ETI presence in the universe (an obviously intelligent signal with no content) will ever be found during our present stage of development.

Yet even this would affect us greatly. Evidence of alien beings beyond our boundaries might act like a catalyst, awakening our awareness of the human situation. People everywhere, for the first time, could see themselves as one species. While religions and politics divide us, an ETI presence could unite us.

Some would fear an ETI signal. 'If the cosmic telephone rings, for God's sake let us not answer,' said Professor Zolenek Topal not long ago. Some would welcome the signal with enthusiasm as a turning point in human history. All would sense a power beyond ourselves, and an outside power has always made us one with our neighbours. We might even respond to the Einstein–Russell appeal, made shortly before Einstein's death, to 'remember that you belong to the human race and forget the rest'.

Perhaps we are still somewhat like our ancestors, the man-apes of the African savannahs a few million years ago, who huddled together in the chill of night watching the stars overhead. We also gaze at the stars but ponder such questions as 'Are we unique?', 'Are there other technological species in the universe?' and 'Are we perhaps surrounded by civilisations beyond our understanding and powers of detection?'

Whatever the answers to these questions, we feel that being one type of self-conscious creature among millions in the universe is decidedly different from being alone in the universe – we don't want to be the most unlikely accident in time and space. But maybe we are something in between these two extremes. SETI is the only way towards finding an answer.

Failure to discover evidence of ETIs after a long search could indicate that one of the essential steps to our existence was very unlikely. For example, the evolution of large brains capable of developing technology may hardly ever be selected for in nature because of the very high energy requirements of brains. The odds against the evolution of a technological species might be too great for such an event to occur more than once in the history of a galaxy of stars. We can view our past and probable future, from the origin of life to our colonisation of the stars, and we can see that the absence of just one stage of the journey makes the complete journey impossible. Yet we have already completed part of the journey, whether it be by chance or by some inevitable unfolding of a universal process. Can anything now stop us reaching the stars? It could be impossible, and what will be impossible in our future would have been impossible for other species in the past.

Which answer would we choose to be true? Perhaps the most acceptable reality for us would be that all technologically intelligent creatures eventually meet a low technological ceiling because there are no more fundamental aspects of nature that can be discovered and applied. The ceiling might be so low that interstellar flight, even by automatic spacecraft is rarely undertaken. Though even with a high technological ceiling, all flights to the stars may be made by automatic spacecraft. One cannot imagine highly intelligent beings spending their lives crossing the light-years in order to investigate other planetary systems when their knowledge of space technology would make it possible for advanced computers to do the job for them.

Alternatively, it seems to me that if technology has a high ceiling, or none at all, if an unlimited flow of applicable knowledge could be discovered in nature, then by now the Galaxy should be well colonised. But if the ceiling is low, then many technological civilisations may go into space and explore their own planetary systems yet not go on to reach the stars. Here, I think, is the key to our best answer. If interstellar travel is practical and can become a routine activity, then we would be in an 'all situation', that is a colonised Galaxy. Otherwise, in view of current scientific information, my guess is that ETIs are rare and widely separated because the planets on which they can evolve are rare and widely separated. It took a few billion years from the origin of micro-organisms for human life to

159

evolve, the first technological species, and we can suppose that it took a similar length of time for other civilised beings elsewhere in the Universe.

So why no sign of colonisation in the Solar System? The asteroids, an attractive source of building materials for ETI space colonies, exist in abundance for our use one day, and the surfaces of Mars and the Moon look as virginal as the driven snow. Maybe everything has been left simply because planets like ours are very rare. Those rare planetary systems in the Galaxy which can produce a new technological species may be left undisturbed. The ETIs would know from their own experience that new technological species can only survive and advance by migrating into space. They may therefore have left us all the building materials of the Solar System as an essential resource for our migration into space. As O'Neill has pointed out, the resources within the Solar System should allow the continued growth of our civilisations for the next 5,000 years. Enough time perhaps to develop social and political stability and the science and technology to move on to the stars. Without this option, our civilisation might never be able to reach the stars.

A question frequently asked is: 'As such a line of progress could obviously have led to colonisation in the past, why have we no evidence of it in the Solar System?'

The best way to look at this problem, I think, is to imagine ourselves outside the Galaxy, trying to guess the answer. Imagine we know everything that we do at present except one thing: we do not know whether or not human beings have detected evidence of colonisation within the Solar System or among our neighbourhood stars. Would we conclude that the Galaxy has been colonised after a few billion years of possible advanced technology and interstellar travel, or would we conclude that there has been no widespread colonisation? I think we would conclude that colonisation is the more probable of these two alternatives.

Now, while we are still outside the Galaxy and guessing, let us be given the information that has been withheld from us: that human beings have not detected any evidence of extraterrestrial intelligence. Would this additional piece of information change our first conclusion? Would we think that this information indicated that the Galaxy has not, after all, been colonised during the past few billion years, or would we think that human beings after only a few decades of space technology (including all the techniques of modern astronomy) have not yet had enough time to discover the evidence? I believe that most of us would back the second alternative; that evidence is there but that we haven't discovered it yet, rather than that it is not there at all. Having said this, if interstellar travel is not common then ETIs are probably thousands of light-years apart and can never visit each other.

I remember three astronomers being interviewed on television many years ago about the origin of the universe. At that time, astronomers were about equally divided in their support for the 'big bang' and 'steady state' theories of the universe. The observational evidence then wasn't adequate enough for them to reach a decision one way or the other. One astronomer supported the one theory; one supported the other; and there was an enthusiastic discussion about which was correct. After a while, the interviewer turned to the third astronomer who had been listening quietly. Which theory, the interviewer asked, did he think was correct? 'The one we haven't thought of yet,' he replied. Instantly, our intellectual feet touched solid ground.

Judging by the history of science, the third astronomer has the best chance of being right. And so it may be with us. The answer to Fermi's question 'Where is everybody?' could be the one we haven't thought of yet. If you think of it, patient reader, do write and let me know.

Recommended Books and Associations

Allen, J. and Nelson, M., *Space Biospheres*, Arizona, Synergetic Press Inc., 1986. A concise account of research in progress to establish closed ecosystems for permanent human habitation in space colonies and on the Moon and Mars.

Asimov, I., *Extraterrestrial Civilizations*, N.Y., Crown Publishers, 1979.

Baird, J.C., *The Inner Limits of Outer Space*, University Press of New England, 1987. A review of SETI by a Professor of Psychology who considers the human factors which motivate the searchers and questions the validity of some assumptions.

Billingham, J., *Life in the Universe*, the MIT Press, 1979. An extensive collection of papers (some technical) given at the 'Life in the Universe' conference held by NASA in 1979.

Bracewell, R.N., *The Galactic Club*, W.H. Freeman and Company, 1975.

Goldsmith, D. and Owen, Tobias, *The Search for Life in the Universe*, Benjamin/Cummings, California, 1980. Extensively illustrated.

Horowitz, N.H., *To Utopia and Back – The Search for Life in the Solar System*, W.H. Freeman and Company, 1986. An examination of the prospects for life elsewhere in the Solar System by one of the scientists who has been leading NASA's investigations.

McDonough, T.R., *The Search for Extraterrestrial Intelligence – Listening for Life in the Cosmos*, John Wiley & Sons, New York, 1987. Extensively illustrated.

Morrison, Philip, *et al.* (eds), *The Search for Extraterrestrial Intelligence*, published by NASA, 1977. Reports the findings of the SETI workshops held at the Ames Research Center, California. Technical.

O'Neill, G.K., *The High Frontier*, William Morrow of New York and Corgi Books, 1976. A book on the colonisation of space by the scientist who showed that space colonies were no longer confined to science fiction. A detailed but non-technical treatment of the subject.

Papagiannis, M.D. (ed), *The Search for Extraterrestrial Life: Recent Developments*, D. Reidel Publishing Company, 1985. The proceedings of the symposium held at Boston University in 1984. A large collection of papers, some rather technical, on many aspects of SETI.

Regis, E.Jr. (ed), *Extraterrestrials – Science and Alien Intelligence*, Cambridge University Press, 1985. A collection of original and reprinted articles.

Ridpath, I., *Messages from the Stars*, Fontana Books and Harper & Row of New York, 1978.

Sagan, C. (ed), *Communication with Extraterrestrial Intelligence*, The MIT Press, Massachusetts. A collection of papers given at the symposium at the Byurakan Astrophysical Observatory, USSR.

Sagan, C., *Cosmic Connection*, Anchor Press and Hodder & Stoughton, 1973.

Sagan, C., *Cosmos*, Random House and Futura, 1980. The book of the television series by the same name. Deals with studies of life and the universe which everyone interested in SETI must consider.

Associations which promote space research and SETI

British Interplanetary Society, 27/29 South Lambeth Road, London, SW8 1SZ. Has a long established reputation for the promotion of astronautics and related subjects. Publishes a monthly magazine and a quarterly technical journal. Both these publications sometimes deal with SETI and related subjects.

National Space Society, International Space Center, 922 Pennsylvania Avenue, S.E., Washington, D.C. 20003. Promotes the exploration of the Solar System and the applications of space technology – both current activities and plans for the future. Issues an illustrated monthly magazine, 'Space World'.

The Planetary Society, 65 N. Catalina Avenue, Pasadena, CA 91106. Actively supports SETI and the exploration of the Solar System. Has over one hundred thousand members worldwide. It publishes an illustrated magazine, 'The Planetary Report,' six times a year.

SETI Institute, 101 First Street, # 410, Los Altos, California 94022. Formed in 1984, it 'promotes research and related activities regarding the search for extraterrestrial life, particularly intelligent life . . .'.

Space Studies Institute, P.O. Box 82, Princeton, New Jersey 08540. Established by Gerard O'Neill who first showed the technical feasibility of space colonies. Supports research projects associated with the technology of space colonisation, and publishes its own journal.

Index